Children of Freedom

Children of Freedom

BY LIBBIE L. BRAVERMAN

Illustrations by
Jessie B. Robinson

NEW YORK
BLOCH PUBLISHING COMPANY
"The Jewish Book Concern"
1953

PRINTED IN THE UNITED STATES OF AMERICA

BY GANIS & HARRIS, NEW YORK

Acknowledgments

The author wishes to acknowledge with gratitude the invaluable assistance of Rabbi Samuel M. Silver and of Ruth Sicherman who made many helpful suggestions; to David Breslau of Bet Berl, Israel, who checked the manuscript for authenticity; to Dorothy Turkel who tried it out in a classroom situation in her seventh grade classes at the Euclid Avenue Temple Religious School.

Foreword

This is the record of the story enacted by the Children of Israel. The dreams, the hopes, the longing of the people described through our history have come true in our lifetime.

The children of today are entitled to know the story of the modern Exodus to the new-old land—to witness the transformation of a persecuted, enslaved people into a nation of free men.

History repeats itself as the liberated men rededicate themselves to building a land whose foundation stones are the ethical precepts of the Jewish faith. Often, in the text, the new story reveals itself as part of the continuity of the ancient history of the Jewish people as it roots itself in the Biblical setting. Frequently, the parallel between the American struggle for independence and the Israeli fight for liberation is strikingly apparent.

In teaching modern Jewish history, it is essential to expand on this most creative phase in contemporary Jewish life. This book is written on Junior High level and belongs in the seventh or eighth grade, depending on where it can be integrated into the curriculum.

LIBBIE L. BRAVERMAN

Table of Contents

Children of Freedom

THE PROMISE—THE FULFILLMENT

And God said unto Abraham.

"TO YOUR SEED WILL I GIVE THIS LAND."

Genesis 12:7

And God said unto Isaac:

"UNTO YOU AND UNTO YOUR SEED I WILL
GIVE ALL THESE LANDS, AND I WILL
ESTABLISH THE OATH WHICH I SWORE
UNTO ABRAHAM THY FATHER."

Genesis 26:3

And unto Jacob God said:

"AND I WILL GIVE THIS LAND TO YOUR
SEED AFTER YOU AS AN EVERLASTING
POSSESSION."

Genesis 28:13

"And I will make them one nation in the land upon the
mountains of Israel . . . And they shall dwell in the land
that I have given unto Jacob my servant, wherein your
fathers have dwelt; and they shall dwell therein, even
they, and their children, and their children's children forever. . . ."

Ezekiel 37:22, 25

1. And They Went Up

"FATHER, there's only one place to go. We must not lose any more time."

"Yes, Daniel, for a long time you've been urging us to go to Palestine. It is not easy to uproot an entire family and move so far away."

"But, father, how much longer must we suffer? How much longer must be wander? Everyone says that in Palestine we will be at home." This was not the first time that Daniel and his father had talked this way.

But now, Daniel's father had at last decided to go to

Erets Yisrael. He had been thinking about it for a long time. His son had urged him.

Driven out of Germany, they had found refuge in Hungary where they hoped to find peace. But even here the Nazis caught up with them. It was too late.

The Jews were ordered to the Ghetto. Daniel's mother was ready to go. His father was fearful of the Ghetto, and rightfully so. Little did Daniel's mother dream that from these places, Jews were assembled, groups at a time, and taken off to death-camps.

They appealed to Peter, an old friend of theirs. He could help them because he was not Jewish. That night, they packed what they could, taking only bare necessities of food and clothing, and left. Peter took a chance even being seen with them. He led them to the woods and found a deserted cave. Here he left Daniel, his father, his mother and his two brothers Shimshon and Avram.

They remained in the cave for what seemed an eternity. They dared not appear in the daytime for fear the pursuing Nazis would find them.

It was dark in the cave. They didn't know when the night began or when the day broke. They remained for almost a month. Peter would come, leave food for them, whistle to let them know he had come, and disappear.

One night, the boys slipped out of the cave. Mother was ill. She was dizzy, probably from the continued darkness. Her head ached and her teeth ached. Daniel and Shimshon brought out a little pan, filled it with water, collected a few dry twigs and built a fire to boil the water. Shimshon picked some cherry leaves and brewed a sort of a tea. This the boys brought to their mother to help cure her illness. She said it helped her feel better.

Time passed. Peter came again. This time he told them the entire territory was becoming dangerous. The Nazis were coming back. He had found another place for them.

So, in the still of the night, cautiously and fearfully, the entire family moved to another cave. They remained in this cave until Peter moved them again.

And so, they moved and moved. Each time they took less with them.

It was getting more and more dangerous. But they were always hopeful that some day Peter would bring better news.

After three long months, Peter did come with wonderful news. The war was over! They could return to their home.

They came back. Their home had been pillaged and robbed. Though the war was over, the Jews were still not secure. That was when Daniel's father determined to leave for Erets Yisrael.

It took a long time. Each day they would go to the American Joint Office to inquire about passage. Each day one of the boys would stand in line, only to receive the answer, "Not yet."

One day it happened. It was Shimshon's turn to go. The line was especially long that day. Shimshon thought that he was due for another disappointment. Instead, when he stated his name the lady behind the desk smiled and said, "Tell your father that you and your family have a permit to go to Palestine. Be ready to leave tomorrow at midnight. The government will not permit you to take any money,

and allows very little clothing. All of you report to this
office at ten o'clock tomorrow night."

Joy knew no bounds! How grateful they were! No more
persecution! No more wandering! They only hoped mother
could make the difficult journey.

The boat was very crowded. People from many lands
embarked. The trip was difficult. They suffered many hardships. But it didn't matter. They were on their way to
Erets Yisrael.

They were all taken off the boat and taken by truck to
an immigrant camp. Here they lived in barracks for many
months. At last, they secured a small house in Natanya.
Father went to find work. Mother soon recovered and was
well enough to keep house. The boys went to school. Their
wanderings were over. They were home at last.

2. I Once Was Afraid of a Gong

A GONG sounded in Degania. It was the signal to wash for dinner. As we were on our way to the dining hall, Naomi smiled.

"Why are you smiling?" Daniel asked.

"Well, it wasn't always this way with me, Dan," laughed Naomi. "There was a time, and not so very long ago, when I would jump at the sound of the gong. I would run and hide when I heard that gong."

They had been picking grapes that day. Daniel had come

from Nahariya to this colony to offer his services during
the grape-picking season. Since there is always a shortage
of helpers at this time, even his services were accepted. He
found himself picking these luscious grapes and putting
more into his mouth than into the basket. But that was
only in the beginning. Since then he had been bringing more
and more in his basket. But Naomi always brought twice
as much.

And that day they had been working hard. The hot sun
had been beating down on them all day long. They were
tired and hungry as well. And then the gong sounded. That
was when Naomi made the remark.

"Tell us," Dan asked, "why were you so afraid of a
gong?"

"Well, it's a long story, and I don't like to talk about it.
It brings back memories that I would rather forget. Perhaps
after supper we'll go up to the field near the orchard and
we'll talk."

As soon as supper was over, a few of them found their
way up to the orchard. Dan liked Naomi. She has dark hair
and black eyes, which dance as she talks. He always finds
grape-picking pleasanter when she's around.

"You know," said Naomi, "we came over on a very
crowded boat. I had spent a year in Holland in a Hahshara
Camp getting ready for the great day when I could come
to Israel. There I learned to speak Hebrew and to work on a
farm. Some of the other boys and girls learned trades. You
see, we wanted to be prepared to do our share when we came
to Erets Yisrael. We heard many stories of the deeds of the
Chalutsim who came to rescue our people.

"And at last, the great day came. My number was called! I could embark on this last voyage and come home! All of us were orphans from Roumania, Poland, Hungary, and Germany. We had been brought to this camp to be trained for a new life in Erets Yisrael.

"None of us had fathers or mothers. We knew, though, that the people of Israel would welcome us like parents. We would no longer be orphans.

"And so it was. When our boat approached Haifa, and we saw Mt. Carmel in the distance, we were so still. I clenched my fists and tried not to cry. I just couldn't wait to set foot on the holy ground. We huddled together at the ship's rail, not talking, just thinking, holding back the tears. We weren't going to let anyone see us cry. Someone started the song, the old partisan song that we had sung at camp— "Mir Seinen Do." We were all singing:

> 'Never say, alas, this journey is my last.
> The hour for which we long is not too far.
> Like a dream our tread will echo:
> Here we are!'

"Then came the words of Hatikva. Never had those words meant so much to me."

"You were lucky," said Gideon, who hadn't spoken until now. "You were a 'legal' immigrant because you came in under the British quota. Your ship pulled into Haifa in the bright sunlight of day. You were welcomed by Henrietta Szold, the mother of Youth Aliyah, who met every boatload of children. I was an 'illegal.' I had no other place to go. I had to be smuggled in. We had to remain hidden. The

British Patrol was always on the lookout. Yehoshua, you remember how you and some of your friends left Erets Yisrael in order to save us, how you stole your way into the Hitler lands to smuggle out some of your fellow Jews."

And Yehoshua told of those terrible days. "I almost got caught more than once," he told us. "We had to remain hidden. We could only work in the dark. We had to be careful about making ourselves known, even to our fellow Jews. The Gestapo was always on the lookout. It was a slow, slow process. We had to work underground.

"Night and day we worked. We had to be on the watch as we crossed the boundaries to bring our precious human cargo to the shores of the Mediterranean. But Gideon can tell you the rest. He was one of those we saved."

Gideon was slow to answer. Finally he said, "I don't want to talk about how I got out of Germany. That brings back horrible memories. But how we crossed the blue sea . . . that's different!

"It wasn't a pleasant journey. Our boat was an old, broken-down tub. We boarded it in the black of night. We moved stealthily, in large numbers, not daring to speak. We were bewildered men and women, and children too, scarcely believing that it could be true, that we really had come out of the land of slavery and would soon be free again!

"But we weren't free yet. We might be sighted and caught. Remember how one year, it was 1947, a boat called the Exodus was denied admission to Israel? Instead of sending them to Cyprus, these poor unfortunate people were sent all the way back to a harbor in Germany. I heard the muffled voices of the sailors. They weren't men; they were

boys like Yehoshua. They had left their homes in Erets Yisrael to come and set us free.

"We were off—on the sea of darkness. There were no
stars, no moon, for the dark night was our best friend in the
sea of blackness. We hardly breathed for fear that even
breathing might draw attention to us. And so we sailed
. . . my brothers, our uncle and his friends. Only when
sure that we were safe, they moved among us, patting this
one on the back, talking to that one, and giving all of us the
feeling that somebody did care whether we lived or died.

"During the day, some of us would be on the lookout,
watching and peering through the binoculars. But others,
like Yehoshua, would sit with us, tell us about Erets Yisrael,
tell us about the Chalutsim, and about the new free life.
'Everyone is free there,' they said, 'free to be a Jew and live
as a Jew.'

"This was not easy for me to understand. I kept asking
myself, 'Is it really true? Will I ever get there and breathe
the free air of Erets Yisrael? Will we be stopped? Am I
doomed never to get there?' "

"Well," said Gideon. "Well," he repeated, "we made it."
And a great big smile covered his face. "We reached the
shores of Erets in the black of night. We were not caught.
Our leaders were clever. They knew how to signal their
buddies on shore so the British wouldn't discover us. We
managed to get in. As we approached the shore, we were
singing 'Hatikva,' the song of hope of the Jewish people.
All of us sang, but you couldn't hear a sound. Our hearts
were singing, our souls were rejoicing, but our lips had to
be silent. We reached shore. Comforting arms embraced us.

Firm, strong hands led us to the land. I touched the earth with my hands and then touched my lips as we hummed 'Lihyot am hofshee b'artsenu.' Then I was whisked away in a car to some colony. We were assigned lodging. But I didn't shut my eyes all night. When the sun rose I found myself in this colony, in a room with other lucky ones who had also found their way home."

"It would have been wonderful if Henrietta Szold were still alive," I spoke up. "But she still lives on in the hearts of her children of the Youth Aliyah.

"We know about Henrietta Szold. We have her picture in our cabin," answered Naomi. "Yehoshua, did you know her?"

"Did I know her? Everyone knew her. Everyone in the world. I even know her life history. It is a glorious story. She came here often . . . an energetic little lady with white hair and dark eyes.

"How this tireless woman watched over the children who came to Erets. She was their guardian angel. Whenever a ship arrived bearing its cargo, there she was at the pier, rain or shine. She would not go home until she was certain that every child was taken care of. Do you see how this colony is ready to welcome these boys and girls? Remember this lesson in Hebrew and history, you are getting now, Naomi. Henrietta Szold started all this. Many of our graduates are following careers in other cities, others have gone out to found new colonies.

"As for Henrietta Szold, she never married. Nevertheless, she was 'Mother' to thousands of children rescued from the lands of persecution. Of course, these boys and girls have well repaid the land that gave them a home. Most of these children together with the Sabras made up the backbone of the Israeli army that won us our independence. Through them, Henrietta Szold will never be forgotten in Jewish history."

"She was an American, wasn't she?"

"Yes, Henrietta Szold was born in America, in the city of Baltimore. Her father was a rabbi who always wanted a son, but instead had only daughters. Henrietta became his favorite. She studied with him, and was to him what a son would have been.

"Let's go back to Naomi's story about the gong," interrupted Daniel.

"Oh, no," said Naomi, "let's hear more about Henrietta Szold. My story can wait."

"Well, for a number of years Geveret Szold was secretary of the Jewish Publication Society of America," Yehoshua continued. "She helped other people write and translate books on Jewish subjects. She helped Solomon Schechter, who discovered the famous Geniza in Cairo, and Louis Ginsberg, the well-known author of 'Legends of the Jews.' She was always interested in her own people and was always on the scene when her people needed her. When Russian immigrants, victims of the pogroms of the 1880's, came to the shores of America, she put into practice the great words of Emma Lazarus—'Bring us your tired, your poor, your huddled masses yearning to breathe free.' She helped them settle in the new land of America, to learn its customs, and its language.

"She visited Palestine in 1912, and upon her return

founded Hadassah, the Women's Zionist Organization of America. Hadassah became the synonym for health for it brought many health-giving activities to Erets Yisrael. It provided health centers and hospitals, playgrounds, and even a medical school for doctors and nurses, treating Arab and Jew alike.

"This organization was born at Purim time, so Henrietta Szold called it Hadassah, the Hebrew name for Queen Esther, who freed her people in days of old. Henrietta Szold was the modern Queen Esther who freed thousands of her people from illness and restored them to health. She saved countless children from certain death.

"Unfortunately, she didn't live to see the full realization of her dream, the birth of the nation Israel. But she surely played a large part in its fulfillment.

"You see, the story of her life is the story of her people. From 1860, when she was born, to her dying day, she helped, she guided, she inspired. At every stage, from the massacres of Czarist Russia, to the horrors of Nazi Germany, whether in America or in Palestine, she taught her people how to live with dignity.

"Naomi, I'm sorry I interrupted you, but I just had to tell about Henrietta Szold. Won't you please go on with your story."

"Oh, I don't mind," answered Naomi. "I knew some of the story, but you've given me a better picture of that great lady."

With her black eyes smiling at Daniel, Naomi continued:

"When we came ashore, we had to go through the reception center. Here we were given medical examinations and some of us were treated. I was sent directly to Degania. It was hard at first in my new home. I wanted to be friends with everybody, but I had to be sure that they were really my friends. Suppose there was a spy who might report me. Then all my dreams of freedom would be shattered.

"And then a terrible thing began to happen; three times a day it would happen, the loud and terrifying sound of a gong! I was so frightened I ran away and hid. I wouldn't talk to a soul. Later I was coaxed out, but still I wouldn't talk. After a few days though, I became accustomed to the sound. I'd try to keep on working. I'd shudder, but wouldn't run away. When people asked me why I was so frightened, I wouldn't talk.

"Today I can talk about it. When we were in Auschwitz in those terrible days, whenever a new group of people was taken into the building with the ovens, a gong was sounded. It was loud and terrifying. We shuddered every time we heard it. One day it sounded for my father and mother."

Naomi said no more. Tears welled.

Poor Naomi was probably re-living those horrible days of Nazi persecution. They were too sad to say a word. What could one say? Daniel reached over and gently touched Naomi's hand.

It seemed like a long time before Naomi spoke again.

She smiled through her tears. "But that was when I first came. I've gotten over it now. Now I know that these are all my friends. Their love has made me happy and unafraid. I go to sleep at night glad to wake up tomorrow."

3. Country Roads

WHAT kind of a place is Degania?

It's a Kvutsah, the kind of colony that was the ideal of the pioneer who gave up his personal possessions to win and build the homeland. Degania is one of the experimental colonies founded in the dark and dreary days of the beginning. When Palestine was a land of disease-ridden swamps and barren rocky hillsides, it was the unyielding devotion of these idealists that overcame the hardships of the pioneering days and laid the foundations of the House of Israel.

Each Aliyah brought different types of people. The ex-

iles, by the thousands and tens of thousands, gathered from
all corners of the world to the place that gave them a home.
Most were people who had lived in cities all their lives. Some
were college-educated, with good learning, well-trained;
some had no training at all. But all had one goal—to live in
the sunshine of freedom. For this purpose, they changed
into workers and farmers. They suffered heat and hardship,
they toiled and they built; they defended and they fought;
they sacrificed, and even died, so that Israel might live.

Many Chalutsim settled in colonies—in cooperative colonies, where they became farmers and shepherds. Others
worked in quarries, planted forests, built roads, homes and
barns, schools and factories. Some settled in the cities,
opened stores, established cooperatives, toiled in factories.

Many of these pioneers settled in the Valley of Yizrael—
the Emek. Malaria-ridden swamp areas were cleared. Where
there were barren plains, they reclaimed the lost soil, and
out of the wasteland, they fashioned fertile fields. On the
hillsides, the exposed rocks were covered with soil, and
vineyards and forests were planted.

It was slow, and it was painful. But these people didn't
feel sorry for themselves. They were building the old-new
land. Three major types of agricultural settlements evolved
in Israel: the Moshavah, the Kvutsah and the Moshav
Ovdim.

The Moshavah was the first form of settlement chosen
by the Chaluts. A Moshavah is a community of individual
farm units with privately owned land. Each farmer owns
his own plot and engages his own laborers. He carries the
burden of his own economic problems. The Moshavah re-

sembles an American village, except the houses are not so widely separated. In Israel they are clustered together and each house is surrounded by a garden.

In the Kvutsah, life is different. The Kvutsah is a collective. Here the inhabitants believe that the combined efforts of a group produce better results than the scattered efforts of individuals. Those who conceived the Kvutsah considered themselves the founders of a new social order designed for the building of a nation. Out of the experiences of the colonies fostered by Baron de Rothschild, they learned that philanthropy was not the way. Therefore, they hit upon the collective idea, wherein property, income, work, and risks are shared in common. The profits are not distributed in money, but in the form of products and services. When the products of the colony are sold, money is used to pay off debts or loans, to purchase new machinery, to beautify the settlement and to add to its cultural resources.

Meals, prepared in the kitchen of the Kvutsah, are eaten in the common dining hall. This also serves as the meeting room and the assembly hall. It is the social center of the colony.

In the Kvutsah no one gets paid, but everyone works. Only the younger children, the sick, and the aged are not expected to be producing members of the colony. Even the children in school do their share.

The little children spend most of their time, day and night, in the children's house, where they receive the best of care. They see their parents at the lunch hour, during mid-day recess, and after working hours.

Education is compulsory, and a familiar scene is the

mingling of parents and their children during every recess from work and learning.

The settler in the Kvutsah works according to a schedule set by a special committee. The work assignment is usually based on the interests of the individual member. His day starts early and his hours are long. But as soon as the sun sets, his working day over, he turns to intellectual pursuits. At night he may attend a lecture, read a book, participate in a discussion, or just listen to one. He might even play in the orchestra, whose instruments are purchased by the colony, or sing in the choir, or perhaps go to a concert, or just listen to the radio.

The Kvutsah is one big family, bound together by a common endeavor. The joys and the worries of daily life are mutually shared.

The Moshav Ovdim is like the Kvutsah except that here each family lives separately. In a Moshav Ovdim, each farmer receives an equal parcel of land for himself and his family. He doesn't own the land, but leases it from the Jewish National Fund. The farmer may renew the lease on his land and hand it down to his children, but cannot sell it. Each family cares for its own farm as if it were its personal property.

The Moshav Ovdim farmer owns his house, his livestock, his tools. The heavy machinery needed for farming is owned by the entire colony. There is no hired labor in this type of colony. Each family brings the surplus products of his farm to the T'nuvah, a distribution center. For instance, the farmer delivers his milk, morning and evening. The milk is weighed, the weight recorded, and at the end of the month, the farmer receives a credit check for the milk delivered. How then do they purchase what they need for every day living? Each colony has Tsorhania, where all purchases may be charged.

Buying for the settlement is conducted in a similar manner. Food, clothing, seed, machinery are procured by the purchasing agent of the colony and sold to the farmers at cost. Not only the buying and selling, but everything affecting the group, such as plans for improvement of the colony, advice on which crops to grow, how to tend crops, and even the conduct of civic affairs, is handled on a democratic basis. They even help on each other's farms when assistance is needed. Here education, administration, medical services are provided by, and for, all the people.

The houses line either side of the street in a typical Moshav Ovdim. The orchards and the fields are on the outskirts. In the center of the village stand the school, the library, the stores, the Community House, the Synagogue.

This compact arrangement makes for a close social life and a stronger educational system. Children attend school more easily and much longer than they do in most farm communities in America, where the farms are so widely scattered. In the evenings, the adults attend lectures and study groups. Within the reach of everyone is the centrally located library, where they may stop to read or borrow books. The farmer is well-informed and eager to learn.

On the Sabbath and on holidays, work comes to a standstill. Only the most essential farm duties are performed. There is little traffic on the roads as the farmers, their wives and their children promenade the main road for their Sabbath stroll. One senses the presence of the Sabbath Queen.

4. How Pleasant for Brethren to Live Together

FROM city and village came professors, students, tailors and peddlers all of whom took up new tools and new tasks as they became workers of the soil. Impelled by the ideals they held so dear, doctors became chicken farmers, professors became soil-experts, and peddlers became road-builders. But rarely did the Chaluts forget that his was the People of the Book.

And the people! Such a large variety of them! Take the Sabras (the native born), nicknamed for the cactus, a sturdy plant that grows everywhere in Israel. Like the cactus, they are tough and thorny on the outside, but sweet inside. They are a sturdy lot, proud of their birthright and ready to fight to protect their independence.

Then there are those who came as youngsters of the Youth Aliyah. They have forgotten the countries in which they only knew persecution and sorrow, and, like the Sabras, are integrated into the land that gave them a new life. These orphans found parents and homes in the motherland. They demonstrated their love for their land by fighting for its independence.

And to many thousands of men and women, who came with the ingathering of the exiles from every corner of Europe and North Africa, Israel finally gave a home they could call their own. To these people this was a sacred gift. In return, they stood ready to do their part in reviving the nation.

And then there were those who came from free lands, such as America, Canada, and South Africa, to stake a claim in the land of their forefathers. They came because they wanted to . . . of their own free will. They joined in the adventure of Israel reborn. They came from all corners of the world, all strata of society, all shades of civilization and they have brought back with them their cultural heritage to enrich their new homeland, making this little strip of land an island in the Middle East, rich in the great diversity of its culture and way of life.

The Yemenite Jews, who came from that ancient feudal

country of Yemen, found a wonderful new life in Israel.
Victims of persecution for years, they were considered serfs,
with no legal rights whatever. They had to wear special
clothing, and were treated like the "untouchables" of India.

When they heard of the creation of the Jewish State, the
Yemenites began to flee. Hundreds left the land of bondage
and crossed the mountains and the desert on foot, like the
Israelites of old. But unlike the Israelites, instead of having
the sea part for them, they found waiting for them what
seemed to be a huge eagle, an airplane, that flew them to
Israel. This was called "Operation Magic Carpet." It seemed
truly miraculous to have these planes pick them up at Aden,
and in one jump, fly them to safety and freedom in Israel.
Later, having flown, they became impatient with buses
which could not run in the air.

Many of these poor souls were disease-ridden, as if with
ten plagues. Infectious diseases such as tuberculosis, tra-
choma, and typhoid had to receive immediate treatment.
The children became so undernourished and dehydrated
that, even with immediate treatment, many could not be
saved.

The adults, many unschooled and untrained, happy to
be free, accepted any kind of work. Those who were silver-
smiths undertook to make filagree jewelry, for which the
Yemenites are famous. All had to be taught the art of modern living—how to sleep on a bed, how to eat butter on
bread, and even how to dress. They marvelled at the mira-
cles of the modern age—radio, telephone, beds! They went
to school and learned to live like the other children of Israel.

They even learned to dance the "Hora" to the tune of "Ratsinu, ve'ratsinu, ve'en zot aggada."

And so, in a little while, the Yemenites too became a true part of Israel—at one with the people and its busy, happy, free life.

And the Arabs in Israel still wear the long flowing robes of ancient days. Most of them still live as their forefathers did, in the same mud huts, threshing wheat and tending the sheep as their ancestors had done for 2,000 years.

In the cities of Israel, Jews live no differently than folk in cities of other countries. The children go to schools. Their parents have the benefit of cultural opportunities. They see the best movies. The Israel Symphony Orchestra plays to a large appreciative audience; the Habima Theater produces well-known plays on Biblical themes and on modern subjects; the Ohel, the Mattatai and other theatrical groups furnish additional entertainment for a drama-loving people.

There is rarely an evening in the large cities that doesn't offer music-loving throngs concerts or operas of a high musical caliber.

As a matter of fact, so high are the cultural goals of the Yishuv that one of the first achievements of the people was the founding of the Hebrew University on Mt. Scopus.

And in the colonies—whether it be a Moshav or a Kibbuts, a Moshavah or a Kvutsah or a Moshav Shitufi—the farmer's life may be completely occupied by day with the milking and tending of cows, with digging, plowing, planting, with harvesting, or with just taking food to market. But when the sun sets, he is off to some cultural activity. No farmer is content with knowing just what goes on in his land; he is also eager to know what is going on in the world. Rarely does one find anyone who hasn't a special interest in some field of art, music, drama, or literature.

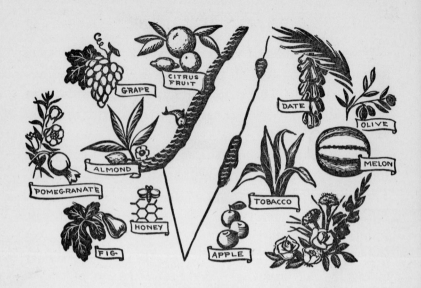

5. Israel's New Look

WHAT kind of a land is Israel? What kind of a climate does it have? Where is it located?

On the map, it is not very impressive. Israel is "squeezed" between the Mediterranean on the west and the Jordan River on the east. It is bounded on the north by Syria and Lebanon, on the east by Jordan, and on the south, beyond the stretches of desert, by Egypt.

The rainfall, except for the wet season, is scanty, and the sun blazes away. Within this tiny area there is located the lowest sea level on earth, whose Dead Sea plunges 1300 feet below.

If you tear a sheet of paper into a rough map of Israel, a long narrow strip torn off the left side will be the Mediterranean sea coast. This strip contains the seaport cities of Haifa and Tel Aviv, which has been coupled with the town of Jaffa.

Now a strip torn along the east boundary becomes the Jordan Valley area, which consists mostly of bodies of water. The Jordan Valley cuts across Israel. Here is found the blue Jordan River, across which, thirty-three centuries ago, Joshua led the children of Israel. It is a swift-flowing river and looks like a blue ribbon as it races its one hundred fifty miles of water from Lake Huleh and the Sea of Galilee passing through Israel and the Kingdom of Jordan down into the Dead Sea.

Next in size to the Jordan is the Yarkon River, which runs north of Tel Aviv and empties into the Mediterranean.

The upper half of this rectangle is a series of hills and valleys, most notably the Emek Yizrael.

Starting on one of the hills where the city of Jerusalem stands, the mountains grow in size until they reach out of Israel to the highest mountain peak on Mount Hermon, which is in Syria.

The lower half of our map is a dry, barren desert called the Negev, which tapers off to Elat, a point on the Red Sea. This barren desert is now dotted with colonies and a water system is making the desert green and fruitful and livable again.

Israel is about the size of the State of New Jersey, 10,000 square miles, about 50 miles at widest and 250 miles long. It has varied climatic areas. The coastal plain is warm and mild;

the Jordan Valley is hot and dry in summer, mild in winter; the hill regions vary in temperature. Israel is subtropical, very much like California. The rainy season begins in October and November and continues until April and May. There is no rainfall between May and October. Abundant dew helps vegetation during the dry season. The temperature rarely descends to the freezing point, so there is no snow in Israel. But in February, 1950, a freak snowstorm did occur, much to the amazement of the inhabitants.

The closest the Israeli normally comes to seeing snow is when the summit of Mount Hermon, in not too distant Syria, is snow-capped.

The mountain areas are divided into two parts. In our history we learn that after the reign of Solomon the Kingdom was divided into two—Judah and Ephraim. The Kingdom of Judah was isolated and stronger. The Kingdom of Ephraim was exposed, an easy prey to Judah. All Judah had to do was travel up the valleys of Ephraim to attack it.

But Ephraim's fields were greener. Judah's area was covered by deep narrow wadis (valleys that once were rivers). The clouds, passing over the high mountains would become cooler and drop all their rain on the hill-tops, leaving the other side of the mountain dry and barren—a desert. Ephraim's area had wider wadis which rose gradually into valleys. They received more moisture. Their valley was therefore greener.

This little country has been the scene of many, many wars. Once it was described as a land of "milk and honey." But migrating tribes invaded the land, cut the trees from its hilly slopes, exhausted the soil, and turned it into a land of swamps and desert, a land deserted and diseased.

Now superhuman efforts and modern methods are restoring some of the former fertility to the soil.

The beginnings were indeed grim. Often one heard complaints and words of discontent. There were many who wanted to give up the experiment, and some even wanted to leave. But others had faith. Those who knew their Bible knew that the once fruitful land could again be made to yield a livelihood. But it would take hard work!

The distinct division of the year into the rainy and dry periods makes Israel an ideal country for cultivation of a variety of fruits. The citrus fruits are the principal products. The oranges, for instance, can ripen to maturity in winter, developing an especially fine flavor.

The ancient methods of plowing and sowing and reaping have given way to the use of modern machinery. Called the Golden Apples, the oranges by the millions are exported each year to all parts of the world. The typical Israel orange is somewhat bigger and longer than the California variety. It has a much thicker skin. In the springtime, the odor of orange blossoms fills the air. The orange-picking season begins in December and ends in April.

The grapefruit, too, is of exceptional quality and flavor and is sold to the continental countries and to England. The Israel etrog (citron), with its delicious aroma, is sent to the Jewries of all the world for the Sukkot festival.

This favorable climate makes mixed farming profitable in Israel. They work the soil all year round, raising winter and summer crops. In the winter season, grain and wheat and barley are grown. Bananas, though almost unknown in Israel before World War I, are now grown on large plantations particularly in the Jordan Valley. All the traditional fruits so frequently referred to in the Bible are harvested today in Israel—figs and dates, grapes and pomegranates. The olive tree, which requires not less than eight years of tending before it blossoms, is bearing fruit that yields good olive oil, so precious to the High Priests in days of old. Deciduous fruits—apples, pears, plums, peaches and apricots—which need cooler climate, are found in the northern part of the country, and also in the outskirts of Jerusalem.

A wide variety of colorful flowers, many mentioned in the Bible, such as the Lily of Sharon, the oleander found on the banks of the Jordan, the beautiful anemones and poppies which make of the fields a carpet in the spring, are abundantly growing again. There are even enough for exports; gladioli, roses and carnations are regularly flown across the sea, and sold in shops from Johannesburg to Chicago the day after leaving Israel.

Millions of trees planted each year, the cypress, the oak, the rock pine, the eucalyptus, the willow beautify the landscape of Israel.

The profusive flowers and fruits of Israel are the living symbols of regenerated Israel. On Friday afternoons, as the inhabitants of the land turn homeward to greet the Sabbath Queen, almost all of them can be seen bearing their floral bouquets with which to bedeck their homes with Sabbath beauty.

6. The Tale of Three Cities

LET'S examine the three principal cities of Israel.
The oldest, as old as history itself, is termed the
city of the past. The youngest, reflecting the new
Israel, is called the city of the present. And the third, once
named the city of the future, has already made good her
promise and becomes larger and more beautiful every day.

The ancient city is the Biblical city of Jerusalem; the
youngest is Tel Aviv; and the one that made good its promise is Haifa. All three are situated within a few hours' travel
of one another. Each has personality of its own; they differ

41

from one another in some particulars but, in others, are as similar as peas in a pod.

Jerusalem is the cradle of Jewish history. In the course of the centuries, the Holy City has been the scene of much violence, all alas, in the name of religion. It is hard to believe that Jerusalem has been conquered thirty-six times, and was almost completely destroyed ten times.

The Bible calls it the City of David, for here King David reigned for thirty-three years. Here his son Solomon built the Holy Temple from wood of the cedars of Lebanon. Fifty years after Nebuchadnezzar (in 586 B.C.E.) conquered Jerusalem, burned the temple, and carried the Jews off captive to Babylonia, Cyrus urged the Jewish people to return to Jerusalem and to build it again.

In the year seventy (70 C.E.) after a bloody siege, Jerusalem was leveled, and again the Temple was reduced to ashes and the ground ploughed up.

It was to Jerusalem that the Crusaders came, massacring a hundred thousand Jews and Moslems, again in the name of religion.

After many years, the British marched into the ancient city, which was yielded to them by the Turks in the least bloody battle of them all. They made Jerusalem the capital. The cradle of the three monotheistic religions was shaken, but the ancient city proudly stood. It was aroused to a new life on its aged foundations.

But a few years later, when the United Nations decided to partition the country, that same Jerusalem, "City of Peace," was again besieged, and again torn by war and bloodshed. Jerusalem, almost entirely encircled by a ring of Arab villages, was cut off from the outside world. The road at Bab el Wad was blocked, and here the bitterest fighting took place. Jewish youths and greybeards carved a circuitous highway through the rocks which they named the "Burma Road," by-passing the Arab villages. And secret caravans brought food to the people who had been reduced to eating grass.

Majestic Jerusalem, the small bit of God's earth stained with the blood of so many millions, is called the Holy City, for it contains sacred shrines of the religions of the Christian, the Jew, and the Moslem. Up to the time of the siege, most of the Arabs, Moslems and Christians and about a thousand Jews, lived inside the thick wall of the old city. The Jews left the old city after a bitter struggle. Today only Arabs, Moslems and Christians live within it.

Old Jerusalem's huge walls, built in 1542, have seven gates, which lead to each of the quarters—the Arab, the former Jewish, and the Christian. It is a city of cobbled lanes and crooked streets, crowded with churches, bazaars and sanctuaries, tiny shops of spice vendors and coppersmiths, sandalmakers and water vendors.

Jerusalem contains the remaining west wall of the ancient Temple, two famous Moslem mosques, Dome of the Rock and Mosque of El-Aksa, and many shrines cherished by Christians. Included in the latter are the Via Dolorosa, the narrow road with its fourteen stations of the cross along which Jesus is said to have walked from the court of Pontius Pilate to the Holy Sepulchre; the rotunda containing his tomb; and the Chamber of the Last Supper.

Outside these walls, a beautiful, modern town surrounds

the ancient city. This is New Jerusalem, mostly built and inhabited by Jews! The contrast between old and new is startling. Instead of cobbled lanes, there are paved streets. Instead of bazaars and booths, there are attractive shops and commercial centers. Instead of Arabs in ancient dress, this suburban section outside the walls is populated by thousands of Jews who call it home and live a happy, busy modern existence. The homes, and even the apartments, contain up-to-date conveniences, reflecting a modern way of life.

Haifa, the second city, is populated by Jew and Arab. For many, many years this site played an important role in history. Its magnificent natural harbor in the Haifa Bay makes it a great shipping center and the terminal for oil pipelines. The top of the mountain, cooled by the Mediterranean breezes, makes Haifa one of Israel's favorite residential sections.

Mount Carmel was a symbol of beauty for poets and prophets. Isaiah called it "Hadar HaCarmel." King Solomon said in the Song of Songs, "Thy head upon thee is like Carmel." It was on Carmel that Elijah triumphed over 450 prophets of Baal and saved the Israelites from idolatry.

Haifa is a stately city and is probably the most cosmopolitan of the Middle East. It is beautiful and majestic with its homes nestling on the slopes of Mount Carmel of Bible fame.

There are three sections to the city. The top is the residential quarter where, on the slopes of the mountain, beautiful modern villas are framed by tall trees and flowering gardens. The middle section, called Hadar HaCarmel, is the center of Jewish life and culture and is a well-stocked shopping section.

The lower town, the port area, is the scene of commercial activity with its shipping headquarters, its tall office buildings and dynamic traffic. Here bearded patriarchs and slender Yemenites and Jews in modern western garb cross the crowded streets as they walk together in a stream of a busy people living creatively.

Not far from the Nesher Cement Factory, the Kaiser Frazer Company is making automobile parts and assembling cars on an eighteen acre site.

The Phoenician Glass Factory, named after the Phoenicians who according to ancient belief, once made glass, manufactures bottles and other glassware.

The best developed industry is the textile industry. Ata weaves and dyes. Textile factories are making shirts and socks and clothing, the basic necessities. Haifa has become the center of chemical industry in the country. The Fertilizer and Chemical Ltd. is making super-phosphate ammoniates, and Kadimah is producing detergents.

Haifa is a vital city. The settlers from the many neighboring colonies come to it for "big city" excitement. Here they find the latest in movies, the best in theater, and the most animated in cafes. Haifa has a large open-air theater where special pageants are presented, the best known being the Bikkurim Festival on Shavuot, which recalls how the first fruits were brought to the Temple in ancient times. In Haifa stands the Technion, a Jewish technological institute where engineers are trained also. Expanding Haifa is often called the "Pittsburgh of Israel," for it is the seat of the country's heavy industry. Modern foundries, engineering shops, and metal works are among its important industries.

The Nesher Cement Factory provides a large portion of Israel's cement requirements. The olive, the sunflower, the flax, linseed, and cocoanut supply oils for the Shemen Oil Factory, which manufactures soap and many toilet articles. Paints based on alcohol and linseed oil are manufactured in Haifa too.

In Atlit, not far from Haifa, are salt works. North of Haifa is the Nur Match Factory. Tobacco firms and furniture shops are among other industries that have sprung up with the influx of the newcomers to Israel.

North of Haifa, near the seashore, is a factory producing electrically welded steel pipes and a steel rolling mill which produces steel sheets and beams for industrial and building purposes.

Where Tel Aviv, the youngest of the three cities, now stands, there were just stretches of sand dunes in the days of the Bible. And so it remained until 1909.

Today Tel Aviv is a gleaming white city, a city with trees and boulevards, a city of modern homes and modern buildings. It has its slum areas but the city planners are constantly devising improvements.

It was in 1909 that a group of Jews, tired of living with the Arabs in the slums of the ancient city of Jaffa, decided to create a suburb. They took for their motto, "I shall build thee and thou shalt be built." They began to erect homes, and laid the foundations of the first all-Jewish city in modern times. They called it Tel Aviv—Mound of Spring.

As the newcomers came, they too erected homes and cultivated gardens. They established a business life, and cultural activities followed. They built a city to meet their needs, one of simple, useful buildings. Utility was their watchword. As merchants, manufacturers, and workers arrived, they opened stores, organized industries, instituted a twentieth century community.

They remembered the friends and heroes of Jewish history, after whom they named their streets and boulevards. Jeremiah, Herzl, Nordau, and Jehuda Halevi, Ahad Ha-Am, Bialik, the Baron de Rothschild and Eliezer ben Yehuda are examples of personalities so honored.

The homes were built to admit the fresh air and sunlight. The roomy balconies and habitable roofs were built so that all the residents could take advantage of the sunshine.

Tel Aviv's streets are paved and well-lighted. The city is stucco-white, and the streets are lined with trees—the palm, and the sycamore, and the acacia. Shrubs and flowers brighten the lawns of the homes in the residential section.

Tel Aviv is a busy city. Its streets are jammed with traffic and with people. Its cafes are always crowded. Stores are gay with window displays. And the beaches have been developed so that people come to spend the day swimming, surf-bathing, or just walking on the boardwalk.

The residents of the city have a wide choice of cultural activities. The Hebrew Theater, the Art Museum, the Israel Symphony Orchestra, lecture halls, and the cinema houses offer programs for every taste.

Each year Tel Aviv sponsors a huge carnival at Purim time, skipped only during war years. It is called the Adloy-

ada Carnival and people come from all parts of the country
to participate or just to observe. The entire city celebrates.
The children masquerade and dress in costume. There are
dances and celebrations, and on Purim day itself, a huge
parade of floats picturesquely proceeds down streets of
Tel Aviv.

Here you see the Kibbuts Galuyot, the gathering of all
the peoples from Eastern Europe, from Yemen, from Germany, from North Africa, from Bulgaria, from Iraq, from
the Americas and from Iran, which in olden days was called
Persia, the scene of the Esther story—all united in their
gay observance of the ancient holiday in the modern manner.

Sports command an American-like enthusiasm in Israel.
Children learn to play soccer, football, basketball, hockey,
volley ball. They learn to run, to wrestle, to jump, to fence,
to box, to swim.

The youth take part in annual swimming meets in Lake
Kineret or in pools throughout the country.

The Maccabee and the Hapoel Sports Associations spon-
sor a variety of athletic events. Each year on Independence
Day, the Ramat Gan Stadium outside of Tel Aviv is the
scene of great sports exhibitions that attract people from
all over the land.

The Sports Associations are invited from time to time to
compete in events all over the world, including the Olympic
games.

The youth of Israel holds its own with the youth of the
world.

7. A Few Lights...
and All Is Quiet

ONE night, they watched it happen. It seems like
a bad dream today. While it was sad and depress-
ing it was, at the same time, exciting.

Shimshon said to Daniel, "Why are you breathing so
hard?"

Let Daniel tell the story, and you'll understand why
both were so excited they could have cried.

It took place one summer, when Abba and Immah had given us permission to work in the gardens of some friends in Nahariya, which you know is a summer resort on the Mediterranean. We were here to help pick fruit. As usual, we ate more than we picked, but together we brought in a good pailful.

It was a beautiful night. Everyone had gone to sleep. But suddenly I was awakened by the sound of footsteps and muffled voices. I was frightened. I got up and peered out of the cabin. I saw people moving about. Shimshon too had been awakened by the noise. We sat huddled together on the doorstep, watching.

And then I saw something. Out at sea was a white speck . . . and the moonbeams played hide-and-seek with it. One moment it was clearly visible, and the next it had disappeared. This was the cause of all the commotion. What could it be? The speck became larger. It was something moving out at sea, but coming closer to shore. Not a word was spoken, but men and women around us were moving busily about. Each one seemed to know exactly what he was doing, but to us it seemed very confusing. The object became larger as it came closer and closer. Then we realized it was a boat—a broken-down tub. The boat was filled with human beings, men, and women, and children, who had lost their homes because of Hitler. They had found their way to the land God promised Abraham thousands of years ago. But how were they going to get ashore? These Olim were really exhausted after all those many years suffering.

"How will they get to shore? I want to help," I whispered, and I started to get up.

"Stay right here and be quiet," said Shimshon, as he pulled me down. "What do you think all the hustle and bustle is about? They know what they're doing! Let's watch!"

And watch we did! And we saw people throw themselves into the sea and swim to the broken-down craft. And then we saw them arrange themselves to form a human bridge. The person nearest the boat picked up a young boy and passed him on. It was like a silent relay race. One person after another, big and little, old and young, was lifted from the boat and transferred from hand to hand and brought to the shore. People stood on the beach ready to help them. They handed these poor souls dry clothing. Silently they removed their wet, clinging rags and put on the dry things.

Before long, the last person had been removed from the boat. The human bridge disappeared as the people moved silently back to shore. All around little flashlights blinked on and off.

Soon we heard the sound of a motor starting. We turned and saw a truck chugging its way up the hill. In a little while, another truckload was moving along too.

In a very few moments, the rescuers returned, entered their cabins, and went back to sleep. Soon all was quiet again.

We, too, Shimshon and I, returned to our cabin. I went back to bed, but I couldn't fall asleep. I don't know how many people had been saved, but I was stunned by what

I had seen. What if they had been caught by the British Motor Patrol? What if a plane had spied them?

And Shimshon said, "A plane did spy another boatload less fortunate. They were caught, and, at gun-point, taken to a British boat, which took them to another camp on the island of Cyprus. Imagine just as they caught sight of the Promised Land, these poor people were sent to further exile in Cyprus."

It was trying for these refugees to be so near their homeland, and yet so far. These people, who had known torture and forced labor, looked longingly toward Israel, only four hours away. Israel sent nurses and doctors and teachers to Cyprus to help them get well and to prepare them for the new land. But many couldn't wait!

Often, in the dark of night, eluding the heavy British guard, they would escape from the concentration camp. More than once, some of the Cyprus natives, Greeks and others, would show them the way to Famagusta, the harbor of Cyprus. Somewhere off shore, a boat would be anchored, waiting for its cargo. And who do you think manned these boats? Our own boys, sailors, like Uncle Yehoshua, who had helped many others escape, plied these boats back and forth. There they would unload their cargo, and return for another load.

It was a long time before we could fall asleep.

But morning came. We were awakened by loud, demanding voices. The British were here.

Sure enough, the British did come around . . . searching, questioning, looking. But there was no trace of a refugee, no sign of the newcomers. It was as though they

had been swallowed up, so completely had they disappeared.
Only the hulk of the broken-down boat remained. It
was allowed to drift out to the sea . . . a sad reminder of
other wanderers who also must find their way home.

8. In Those Days at This Season

JT was Friday, late afternoon (Nov. 29, 1947), at Flushing Meadows, Lake Success, New York. Sunset was fast approaching, and soon the Jewish people would be ushering in the Sabbath.

All these years the Jews had hoped that the world would do justly by them and grant them a "legally secure, pub-

licly recognized homeland." And now the United Nations
was slicing up Palestine, giving one part to the Arabs, and
another to the Jews. The Arab states were not in favor of
giving the Jews any part of Palestine.

A few bearded Jews gathered in a corner of the hall of
the United Nations building and turned toward Mizrach
for evening prayer. At this crucial moment they knew but
one language, the language of prayer.

The discussions carried over into the Sabbath. It was
Sabbath afternoon, and the delegations were voting.

A two-thirds majority was needed. Would the world
representatives brighten what might otherwise be a black
Sabbath, miserable and disappointing? "Yes" sounded like
music, whether it was expressed in French, or Spanish, or
English. The word "no" grated like a discordant note. The
numbers were rising. More delegates were saying "yes"!
Many abstained from voting. But the "yes" votes were
mounting! The Jews were winning. They won! The United
Nations adopted the Resolution! The vote was 33 to 13.
Before the Sabbath was over, the majority of the delegates
had voted in favor of the Resolution. The United Nations
had recommended that Palestine be partitioned!

The news flashed over the radios. At last, a miracle was
to take place. The entire world was electrified at this
Solomon-like decree! Throughout the United States, England and Canada, Jews gathered to sing, to dance, to cele-
brate. Can you imagine what it meant to the Jews in the
camps of Europe? In Israel, of course, there was great rejoicing when the tidings crossed the ocean. Jews danced in
the streets. Just in the Chanuko season too, the miracle

had happened! It was in those days, and at this season, that Jews celebrated their first struggle for freedom! There had not been such a happy welcome extended to Queen Sabbath in many years.

But the celebration didn't last long. The British were determined to block the Jews. The Arabs began shooting, and the Jews had to fight back.

The boys had been trained in the underground. Haganah didn't have the modern weapons of warfare. But that made no difference when Syrian and Lebanese from the north, trans-Jordan and Iraqi troops from the east, swooped down upon them. Egypt moved up from the south and tried to blockade the Mediterranean approaches.

On November 30th, the business center of Jerusalem was looted by Arabs. Jews were killed on the road from Tel Aviv to Jerusalem. During the next few days, the fighting spread to a greater area of Jerusalem, and to other parts of the country.

The Arabs made the road to Jerusalem dangerous for travel, blocking it completely for intervals. It was kept open, but at the cost of many lives.

The road to the Negev was also dangerous for travel. It was even cut entirely for many weeks. That road was forced open too.

The so-called Arab army of "hired" men from Syria, Iraq, and Lebanon brought cannon. They called it a secret weapon. The Jews fought in the face of extreme handicaps. They didn't have an army at all. The British tried to take all their arms away. Many of the men were arrested for carrying weapons and were hauled off to military courts.

The Jews had a secret weapon too. Their weapon wasn't arms. It was "Ein B'reirah"—no alternative. They had to fight. The sea was behind them. They couldn't turn back.

But the Arab hordes who came over from Syria and Lebanon did have an alternative. They could run back . . . and they did.

The Egyptians were invading the Negev. They followed the ancient historical roads, the same routes that the armies of the Kings of Israel, Saul, David and Solomon, had once traveled. They came up from the Red Sea to Beersheba, a little more than fifty miles from Tel Aviv.

The United Nations Resolution of November 29, 1947, had to be carried out. But who would do it? It was up to the people of Israel. The Maccabees of the modern age took up the battle . . . mechanized Maccabees, with tanks, and jeeps, and planes, must hammer out the victory.

Jerusalem had to be saved! The Egyptians had to be driven out of the Negev!

The situation seemed desperate. But the Jews were determined!

A major offensive was conducted in the Negev. When the Egyptians invaded, they hoped to cut the Negev off from the rest of Israel. The Negev campaign was called "Operation Ten Plagues." History was repeated. The Egyptians were beaten, and drowned in the sea of Israel's courage and strategy.

They won fight after fight. The victories mounted. Undaunted, the Israelis forged ahead. "If we do not do so, who will; and if not now, when?" The wise words of the great

Hillel, found in Pirke Ovos, the "Sayings of our Fathers" became more meaningful.

Thus a new chapter was begun in the exciting romance between the people of Israel and the land of Israel. Let's look in on the earlier stages of that story.

9. In the Beginning

FROM the very outset, the land of Israel spelled glamour to the people. When the children of Israel were set free, Moses brought them out of the land of Egypt. He was able to make them bear their hardships by telling them that their destination would be the Promised Land. To bring them there he had to prepare them for nationhood. The tribesmen acquired a constitution, the Torah; they learned how to govern themselves and to live as a nation.

In Canaan the Jewish people was born; here it lived and prospered. Over the Jordan River, Joshua had led the children of Israel into the Promised Land. On the Mount of Gilboa a great battle was fought by the nation's first king, King Saul. On Mount Carmel, the prophet Elijah challenged the idol worshippers to the supreme test of faith and revealed the real God. In Jerusalem arose the Temple of Solomon. When the people strayed from the true path of the law, prophets rebuked them. They solemnly warned that if they did not return to God, they would be driven out of their land.

The prophet Amos, dismayed by the people's weakness and wickedness, prophesied their destruction, but the God of Amos was merciful and held out the hope that after destruction and exile:

"I will bring back
The exiles of My people Israel,
And they shall build the waste cities, and dwell in them."
—Amos 9:14

Israel was driven out of Palestine, as the prophets had predicted. King Nebuchadnezzar led them off captive to Babylon in 586 B.C.E. But the people yearned to return. They were not to be comforted.

"By the rivers of Babylon,
There we sat down, yea, we wept,
When we remembered Zion.
Upon the willows in the midst thereof
We hanged up our harps
For they that led us captive asked of us words of song,
And our tormenters asked of us mirth:
'Sing us one of the songs of Zion,'
How shall we sing the Lord's song
In a foreign land?"

But Isaiah spoke words of consolation.

> "Be comforted, O be comforted, My people,"
>   says your God;
> Bid Jerusalem take heart
>   and proclaim to her,
> That her time of service is ended,
>   that her guilt is paid in full,
> That she has received of the Lord's hand
>   double for all her sins."
>
> —Isaiah 11:1,2

And the prophet Ezekiel urged them to have faith. He dramatized his belief that Israel would live again in the vision of the dead bones come to life.

And not long after, in the year 538 B.C.E., Cyrus, the King of Persia, declared:

> "The Lord, the God of Heavens, has given me all the kingdoms of the earth, and He has charged me to build Him a Temple in Jerusalem which is in Judaea. Whosoever there is among you who belongs to His people (may his God be with him), let him go up to Jerusalem which is in Judaea and build the Temple of the Lord, the God of Israel. And as for those who remain where they dwell, let them help with silver and gold and goods and beasts of burden as well as with free-will offerings for the Temple of the Lord in Jerusalem."

Thus occurred the First Return. And soon the Second Commonwealth was established. The wanderers were determined to rebuild the land and to re-enthrone the Torah. Ezra, the Scribe, helped build the wall of the spirit—the Torah. Nehemiah helped build the wall of stone. Together they helped rebuild the nation.

And the land of Judea again swarmed with people. They crowded the towns and the cities. They rebuilt the Temple. Once more inspiration flowed from the Temple and the priests. At festival times they made pilgrimages to Jerusalem to rejoice in the Temple.

But again the land was invaded. In the year seventy, another enemy attempted to destroy it. The Roman conqueror Titus sought to destroy the children of Israel. He burned the Temple and dispersed the people. And the once teeming city became a ghost town and the musical language of the people in Jerusalem was stilled. A remnant of Jews remained in other cities of the devastated homeland. The rest, scattered to the corners of the world, had but one thought. Wherever they were, whatever their condition, they never stopped praying for the day they would return to Judea. They remembered the west wall, all that remained of Solomon's Temple. They remembered Jerusalem with its hills and its valleys. Never, never did they forget their Holy City. Regularly they recited the Psalm: "If I forget thee, O Jerusalem, let my right hand lose its cunning and my tongue cleave to the roof of my mouth" as a pledge that they would return. In the two thousand years of exile, Jews prayed daily to return to the land that God promised to Abraham, Isaac and Jacob.

Generation after generation prayed and hoped to return and re-create, as Ezra and Nehemiah had done.

But it was not until two thousand years later that the people began to trickle back to join those who had remained.

After World War I, history repeated itself, for another

Cyrus-like declaration, this time the Balfour Declaration, called a wandering people home. Lord Rothschild, as President of the English Zionist Federation, received the communication from Arthur James Balfour, the Secretary of State for Foreign Affairs:

"His Majesty's Government view with favor the establishment in Palestine of a national home for the Jewish people, and will use their best endeavors to facilitate the achievement of this object."

Approved by the cabinet, this augured well the realization of the dream of Theodore Herzl, and the hope of the Jewish people never abandoned in 2000 years of exile and persecution. The pronouncement was hailed by Jews throughout the world with thanksgiving and joy.

The years of exile were now drawing to a close. The Balfour Declaration encouraged the Jewish people to return and to rebuild the Jewish Homeland.

And after World War II, the United Nations adopted the resolution which recommended the partition of Palestine and the establishment of a Jewish State. That very week, the Haftorah reading included the prophecy of Amos,

> "In that day I will raise up
> The tabernacle of David that is fallen;
> I will wall up its ruins,
> And close up its beaches,
> And I will rebuild it as in the days of old . . .
> I will bring back
> The exiles of My people Israel,
> And they shall build the waste cities, and dwell in them,
> And they shall plant vineyards, and drink their wine;
> They shall also make gardens, and eat their fruit.

And I will plant them upon their land,
And they shall no more be uprooted
From the land which I have given them,"
Says the Lord,
Your God.

—Amos 9: 11, 14-15

And the third Jewish Commonwealth was born. And the Jewish State proclaimed its independence on Iyar 5,5708 —May 14, 1948.

And the cities again swarmed with people and throbbed with life. A colorful musical language once more filled the air . . .

"Bid Jerusalem take heart
and proclaim to her,
That her time of bondage is ended."

—Isaiah 40:2

10. The Hope That Would Not Die

DETERMINED to destroy the Jewish people, Titus burned the Temple, and dispersed the Jews to the far corners of the earth. He returned to Rome and built an arch of triumph bearing his name as a permanent monument to his victory. But the arch has been discredited, Titus forgotten, and the Jewish people lives on. Of Solomon's Temple, only the Western Wall remains as a

relic of Israel's glory . . . a shrine to which Jews returned
to wail and pray. Of the people, a small remnant remained
in Judea throughout the centuries. It was destined, however, that the promise made to Abraham, Isaac and Jacob
would be redeemed. Titus did not succeed in uprooting the
people from the land. Wherever they lived, Jews throughout the world enshrined the dream of the restoration of
the Jewish nation in their hearts and in their prayers.

Yehuda Halevi, a renowned poet of medieval days, prayed,
and dreamed too. He wrote poetry full of yearning for
Zion. One that is sung by Jews to this day is "My heart is
in the East."

> "My heart is in the east, and I in the uttermost west—
> How can I find savor in food?
> How shall it be sweet to me?
> How shall I render my vows and my bonds,
> While yet Zion lieth beneath the fetter of Edom,
> And I in Arab chains?
> A light thing would it seem to me
> To leave all the good things in Spain—
> Seeing how precious in mine eyes it is
> To behold the dust of the desolate sanctuary."
>
> (*Translation*, Nina Salaman)

Like the Chalutsim of our day, he translated his longing
into action and returned to the Land of his Fathers.

Legend tells us that he decided to leave his only daughter
and his many friends in order to settle in the city he loved.
He succeeded in coming close enough to see it. Reciting one
of his great poems about Zion, he approached the city
proper. As he was about to enter the holy city, an Arab

pierced him with a lance. Like Moses, he saw his Promised Land but was not privileged to enter.

Many Jews who couldn't return to the homeland to live were content if they could die there. But many thousands found their way back, not to die, but to live again in Israel.

Persecution and cruel treatment in the countries of Europe throughout the centuries intensified the desire of the Jews to return to the Homeland.

Because of this, false messiahs were able to arouse the people to uproot themselves from these countries of oppression.

Now the people began to receive inspiration and new hope which led to concrete action. One of the earliest of the writers who urged the return was Moses Hess. He had formerly believed in assimilation as a solution of the Jewish problem. But he changed his mind and wrote a remarkable book called *Rome and Jerusalem*. In it he asserted that every people had a right to live in its homeland. He urged mankind to help the Jews re-establish their nation.

After Alexander II of Russia was assassinated in 1881, a wave of pogroms took place in that hate-ridden country. Many Jews hoped to escape by assimilating, but others realized that assimilation was not the answer. They saw that there was no future for them in Russia. Thousands of Jews migrated to the United States. But many chose the road that led them back to the Promised Land.

It was the writing of another book, actually only a pamphlet, that created a great stir. It was written by Dr. Leo Pinsker, a physician, who also believed in assimilation. It was called *Auto Emancipation,* and in it he declared that assimilation was *not* the solution. "We must emancipate ourselves," he wrote. "We must rely on no one but ourselves." Written when Alexander was still Czar, it called on the Jews to free themselves, and to ask the people of the world for a homeland. His call electrified the existing Hovevei Tsiyon and aroused them to action. Many rallied to the cause.

Their slogan, "Bilu," was made up of the first Hebrew letters of the words in which the prophet Isaiah called out to his people: "Bet Yaakov L'hu V'naleha"—"O House of Jacob, come let us go."

This cry brought many people out of the lands of persecution. They went up to the Promised Land. They were the first Aliyah.

At first they settled in towns, content only to reside on the beloved soil. Then they founded colonies. They created Petah Tikvah, Rishon L'Zion, Zihron Yaakov, Rosh Pinah, Gedera. They suffered hunger, sickness, loneliness. They almost abandoned the idea. Baron Edmond de Rothschild, the great philanthropist, saved them from going under. They rallied, they struggled, grew old. But these pioneers demonstrated the will to return. The next Aliyah would continue what they had started.

Among the men and women who had responded to the new call were students imbued with the idea of working the land. They would again make it flow with milk and honey. They came without money, without training, but with an invincible love. They felt that destiny had brought them back to rebuild. They gave up their personal belongings and even their private lives. They were all going to work together as one, cooperatively, for the great ideal. This they did magnificently. This was the way they chose to work, and to live too. They called each colony a Kvutsah. Degania was the first such colony to be founded (in 1909) and is now termed Aym haK'vutsot.

Even before these settlements were fashioned, another small book was written and it generated even greater interest and later, much activity. Theodore Herzl had never heard of Hess, or of Pinsker. His book, *The Judenstaat*, expressed the very same ideas. "We are a people—our people. Let us return and rebuild the Jewish State! The Jewish problem can only be solved," he called out, "through the collective efforts of the Jews themselves." As the prophet Ezekiel, of the Babylonian exile, drew a complete plan for the new Temple, so Herzl, in his day, produced a blueprint of the reborn Jewish State.

Inspired by Herzl, wave upon wave of Jews found their way back to Zion. After World War I, in 1917, the League of Nations gave England the Mandate for Palestine, instructing her to help the Jewish people "reconstitute their national home."

Men and women from countries of Europe came to the old-new land—unskilled workers, traders, artisans, professors, students, people of all kinds, some of them practical and many were just visionaries. They were the Chalutsim. They were the people of destiny. They translated the prayers, the dreams of generations into the reality of reclaiming the soil, of re-creating the nation. They were determined to lift the Jewish people to nationhood.

A third Aliyah followed. They laid the foundations for

Jewish self-government. These people came better prepared, physically and psychologically. They established more co-operative settlements. They founded the Asefat haNivharim and the Vaad haLeumi of Knesset Yisrael, the Jewish community.

The fourth wave was the tidal wave. It exceeded all expectations. People came from Russia, Ukraine, Roumania, Lithuania, Poland and from the United States. Some with money, and some with nothing but ideals! They drained the swamps; they built the settlements and the factories.

When Hitler, the Haman of modern times, came into power, increasing numbers sought refuge in Palestine. Britain, which still held the mandate, piled up obstacles for the refugees. The British imposed quotas limiting immigration, just when the number of people desperately seeking entrance rose from day to day.

Two kinds of Aliyah developed—Aliyah Alef, the limited "legal" immigration, which England permitted, and Aliyah Bet, the so-called "illegal" immigration, without benefit of certificate.

The people of Palestine staked everything, even their lives, to help those who were forced to "steal" into the Jewish homeland. For it was life or death for the immigrants fleeing from the gas chambers of Hitler.

The story of Youth Aliyah is a separate series of dramatic chapters in our history. It was a huge project lasting many years and it saved children from certain death.

And the Jewish National Home continued to flourish. From just a handful of people, the population mounted until it reached hundreds of thousands, who plowed and sowed, broke rock, and built roads, planted trees and re-deemed the land. They were breathing life into a soil dead for generations. They were re-kindling the spirit of a people. This soil, this people—together—were to constitute the Third Jewish Commonwealth.

11. The Name of Our State Shall Be Israel

THE British Tommies were busy moving for days.
They took everything they could possibly lift,
and loaded their ships.

No one was sorry to see them go. They had caused so
much trouble.

The day the British left Haifa was a happy one. The
Union Jack came down. The High Commissioner was
hardly out of Haifa Harbor, when the Jewish soldiers raised
the blue-white flag. The flag that had always been the sym-

bol of future glory, that day, became the symbol of the
freedom at last attained. People gathered to watch.

As the flag unfurled they sang the Hatikva with such
fervor that it seemed they were trying to blow the British
ships into the sea with their voices.

Before leaving on May 14, 1948, the British had inflicted
great damage. They destroyed official records. They dis-
mantled machinery of government. Anyone caught with
arms had been disarmed, and it was often proved that these
same arms later found their way to Arab hands.

But finally, the British were actually leaving, as they had
been threatening to do for a long time. The High Commissioner and his entire entourage had slipped out of Haifa
Harbor. Now, finally, they were gone!

The Jews were ready! The flag of Israel was hoisted to
announce to the world that the Jews were in possession of
Haifa! Not a moment elapsed between the British evacua-
tion and Jewish independent action.

In addition to all the destruction and sabotage they
inflicted, the British placed the Arabs in strategic points,
even in areas near Jewish settlements, and the British had
supplied them with ammunition. But many Arabs lacked
the courage to fight, and fled.

At the same moment in Tel Aviv, the State of Israel was
born. Over Kol-Yisrael, the national radio network, David
Ben Gurion, issued a call to the members of the National
Council.

What could it mean? On Friday too! No one calls a meeting on Friday! It must be something important! The scene
was at the Tel Aviv Municipal Museum. Before long the

place was filled, and soon it was surrounded by men and women clamoring to get in.

There was a long table on the platform, at which sat David Ben Gurion. On either side of him were members of the Provisional Council. The representatives of the Jewish people in Israel as well as members of the Jewish Agency came. Above hung the picture of Theodore Herzl, whose fifty-year-old dream was being realized almost to the day.

David Ben Gurion rose. A hush fell over the audience as he proclaimed, "THE NAME OF OUR STATE SHALL BE IS-RAEL!" Thus was the new nation born.

Who will ever forget the words of the Declaration which followed:

"The land of Israel was the birthplace of the Jewish people. Here their spiritual, religious, and national identity was formed. Here they achieved independence and created a culture of national and universal significance. Here they wrote and gave the Bible to the world. . . . It is the natural right of the Jewish people to lead, as do all other nations, an independent existence in its sovereign state. . . . Accordingly we, the members of the National Council, representing the Jewish people in Palestine and the World Zionist Movement, are met together in solemn assembly today, the day of termination of the British mandate for Palestine; and by virtue of the natural and historic right of the Jewish people and of the Resolution of the United Nations, we hereby proclaim the establishment of the Jewish State in Palestine, to be called M'dinat Yisrael. . . ."

History was being made. Those words broke the exile of 2,000 years. The land God promised to Abraham, Isaac and Jacob was being returned. These were the words that proclaimed to the world that the people of Israel was free. In Ben Gurion's historic address the nations of the world were asked for official recognition and assistance.

Slowly and reverently the people left the Hall, citizens of a new State. It was Erev Shabbat. Everyone was happy, but solemn too. Queen Sabbath was about to arrive, and the new Israel was preparing to greet her.

All of the city's inhabitants were out-of-doors. Only Uri's mother didn't come out. Uri had died in action. She didn't cry. All she said was, "What a pity Uri couldn't have lived to enjoy this moment."

There were many others missing too. They had given their lives so that this could happen.

That was why people were joyful and, at the same time, very thoughtful.

Someone started the Palmach song, and like magic many more joined them. They sensed that others shared their song of victory—the Jews in all the world—and they were right. The news of Israel's independence set off a chain reaction of music in the hearts of Jews everywhere.

The prophecy of Dr. Theodore Herzl came alive that day. In his diary, in 1897, he wrote, "In Basle I founded the Jewish State. If I were to say this today, I would be met with universal laughter. In fifty years, everyone will see it." And so, fifty years later, it came to pass.

Herzl's life story reads like that of a prophet. As a youth, he showed great literary promise. At an early age he wrote for a Vienna newspaper called the "Neue Freie Presse." He authored short stories and plays, which quickly made him famous. Then he was sent as a foreign correspondent to

Paris. He was assigned the Dreyfus trial, an event which was destined to change his whole life. The newspapers were full of the story. The headlines carried the news that an officer in the French Army had been accused of treason.

Herzl was struck by the fact that these people were bent on convicting this young captain, guilty or not, because he was a Jew! Whenever the prisoner was led to the courtroom, or back to jail, people lined the streets and kept crying "Jew! Jew! Down with the Jews!" He was alarmed at the hatred manifested against the Jews. Herzl became convinced that Dreyfus was an innocent victim of prejudice. Dreyfus was convicted, stripped of his military honors and sentenced to Devil's Island.

Herzl was beside himself. He could not sit, nor stand, nor sleep. It was as if he heard the voice of God calling to him to come to the aid of his people. Like the prophet of old, he answered the call. He could no longer continue as a reporter. He became imbued with the idea that the Jewish people must have a State of their own.

Almost overnight, he wrote a book called the *Judenstaat*. He forgot about his reporting, his family, and even himself. He set to work to do what he could to create the Jewish State.

He called on kings and emperors, and on the Sultan of Turkey. He brought the Jewish problem and his suggestion for its solution, before men of high rank and influence.

He sought the help of friendly governments. They listened to his story, but many did not understand the greatness of his plan. Often was he ridiculed, often subjected to scorn and mockery. In his travels he saw the misery of Jews in other lands. When he came to Russia, the people hailed him as a Messiah! Occasionally the great powers gave him some hope . . . but never real help.

Herzl summoned the Jews of the world to a World Zionist Congress, at Basle, Switzerland, the first of its kind. He displayed the perseverance of an idealist, and the diplomacy of a statesman. He dedicated his life to this idea, which became almost an obsession with him until the last day of his all too brief life.

And now, a half century later, his prophecy was realized: "If you will it, it is no dream." Half a century later, the Jewish people were recognized as a nation. They now had the Jewish State of which Herzl dreamed.

And Theodore Herzl took the journey home too. His earthly remains were brought from Vienna back to Israel— to the Jewish State. The mountain where he was buried took his name and is called Mount Herzl.

But not so fast. The celebration was short-lived. The very next morning, while our new Israel was basking in the calm of Shabbat peace, and still under the magic spell of the great event, the people were awakened by the drone of airplanes and the dropping of bombs.

In Tel Aviv, the air-raid wardens issued orders for all to stay indoors. The radio announced: "It is war again! Those are Egyptian planes overhead. Blackout laws will be observed. Prepare the air raid shelters! On the alert!"

The hymns of thanksgiving were interrupted by the roars of war. Herzl's dream had to wait before it would be completely fulfilled.

12. The Spirit of '48

THE Arab armies were massing at the borders! King Abdullah hurled his Arab Legion against Jerusalem. His fellow Arabs had already cut Jerusalem off from the coast by blocking the road to Tel Aviv.

The Arab Legionnaires were pouring through St. Stephen's Gate, along the Via Dolorosa, the road where Jesus is said to have carried the cross to Calvary. The venerable city, where the world's most sacred shrines are located, was being attacked by artillery fire. The Arab Army led by Glubb Pasha, a British General, was attacking the holy places. The Wailing Wall, the Moslem Dome of the Rock, where Abraham is said to have brought Isaac for the sacrifice, were in the line of fire.

The people in Jerusalem were trapped. The Arab Legion closed the gates to the City of David. Jerusalem lay under siege. The supply lines were cut, and no food or water could be brought into the city.

But they were ready. The Israel soldiers fought to protect Jerusalem and its holy places.

Convoy after convoy was assailed. They were afraid the blockaded Jerusalemites were faced with a lingering death.

Many were the acts of heroism in those days of war.

Avram was only sixteen years old, but was determined to fight. So, for army purposes, he was eighteen. He volunteered, and was attached to the Jerusalem unit. Out on a mission one day, the vehicle he was driving was blown up. And the next thing he knew, he woke up in the hospital. His mother says he didn't know then that he had lost his leg. He had but one desire. He must return to his post. The war had to be won, and he must fight it. Avram might have lost his leg, but not his courage.

Naomi sold handbags in a leather goods shop. She always looked charming and smart in her gold-colored suit. But the night found Naomi on duty in a khaki uniform, with a cartridge belt and binoculars, on the lookout for signs of the enemy.

During the day, Shimshon wore a slick white jacket when he played the accordion and sang gay songs to entertain the hotel guests. He was quite the "smoothy," and a very good entertainer. But at night, he was an entirely different Shimshon. Dressed in baggy khaki, carrying a heavy rifle too big for his size, he stood on duty on the night watch.

And there was Yigal, the hunchback, who sold cigarettes.

He was a listless, unhappy-looking individual. Then he volunteered in the Israeli Army. When he became a soldier, he too was transformed. When he put on that uniform, his shoulders seemed straight, he spoke in a lively manner, and even whistled as he walked. When he fought for his country, he found a new dignity.

And who are these bearded Jews in khaki? Are those "paot" under their steel helmets? They surely are! Many religious Jews joined up. Their early morning prayers helped them more than once to meet the day's work with courage and confidence.

Many were the brave lads who fell. The people mourned the loss of loved ones, but never stopped fighting.

Heroic tales of undaunted faith are told. One is about a Yemenite who earned his living as a porter. Every day, morning and evening, he would come to the Wailing Wall to pray. But even there, no one was safe. Arabs shot at Jews on their way to the Wall. More than one Jew, wearing Talit and Tefilin, was shot down as he prayed. But our Yemenite continued to go to the Wall.

However, when the situation became more critical, the Commander of the Israeli Army declared the Wailing Wall "Out of bounds." And so it became deserted.

"But it is prohibited to desert the Wailing Wall even one day without prayer," wailed Chaim. And each day he would secretly slip out of his house and find his way to the Wall. One day, Chaim was not to be found at home. They searched for him everywhere. Finally, on the tear-stained road leading to the Wailing Wall, he was found . . . shot. They brought him home and tried to nurse him back to health. He was not to be comforted. He prayed only to see the Wailing Wall again.

Then came the truce. The Commander ordered all those who were ill to be removed to new Jerusalem. Against his will, Chaim was taken out of the old city. They carried him to the Hadassah Hospital. He wouldn't eat. He wouldn't talk. The nurses were worried about him. He wanted only one thing—to return.

"The Wailing Wall is our holy of holies," he said. "It is the gate to heaven. The Wailing Wall must not be left without prayer for even one day." And Chaim could not be comforted.

One day Chaim disappeared. The hospital attendants searched for him. Near the Wailing Wall stood some Arab soldiers on duty. They heard a strange sound. They came closer to the sound and discovered a Jew, wrapped in his Talit, praying before the Wailing Wall. They lifted their rifles, but were afraid to shoot.

"His voice seems to penetrate the stones and go straight to heaven," they said.

They didn't touch him. Later, Jewish soldiers found Chaim and brought him back to the hospital. They asked him how he had slipped out of the hospital unobserved. They wondered how he had reached the Wailing Wall undiscovered and returned unharmed. But they never found out.

Chaim fell asleep, and never woke up again. He died happy. He had not abandoned the Wailing Wall.

Israeli soldiers fought to protect the sacred places. The bravery of these modern Maccabees encouraged the inhabitants, and bolstered their resistance.

The Hadassah Hospital on Mount Scopus continued to serve the army and civilians against all odds. A tragic thing happened to Dr. Chaim Yassky, the director of the Rothschild Hadassah University Hospital. He traveled with a convoy of scientific and medical personnel to Mt. Scopus. The Arabs knew that it was a medical convoy but they attacked it nevertheless. Dr. Yassky and seventy-six members of the convoy died on the battlefield in the midst of this errand of mercy. In memory of this great hero, the first hospital built in the Negev after the war was named Yassky Hospital.

Abdullah's men fought on. The Israeli Army continued to defend the ancient city.

And soon, Jerusalem was liberated.

13. Election Day

J T was Election Day in Israel. For the first time in 2,000 years the Jewish people, as a free people, were voting. Today both Jews and Arabs, through the land, were going to the polls. It was proclaimed a national holiday. Up to now, because of the situation, the Provisional or temporary government, a coalition of all the parties, was in power. The census was taken. Identity cards were issued to all men and women over eighteen.

There had been more than the usual election routine. This was the very first time. Again it seemed more like a dream than a reality.

Electioneering had kept the country in a state of excitement. Each city was flooded with posters. Placards covered every wall, every post, and every possible space on buildings. Every street corner had a soap box, every thoroughfare its sound truck, every campaign office its loud speaker. Each party was doing its utmost to get the voters to the polls. In towns, in cities, and even in the remotest colonies, wherever there was a central square, meetings were taking place. They would just set up a microphone, and representatives of each party spoke. The crowds gathered and listened eagerly.

"I wonder if anyone around here hasn't made up his mind yet," said Avram to Daniel, as they stood at the November Second Square, right in the traffic hub of Tel Aviv, listening to a Mapai speaker.

A policeman standing close by said, "It is hard to believe, isn't it? So many parties, so many opinions, so many nationalities . . . each group free to express itself. Fighting with words, but not a single fist fight."

Suddenly we heard a rumbling noise. "Oh, oh, what's that? A truckload of people! Maybe I spoke too soon!"

It was more than just one truck. It was a motor caravan—cars covered with political posters and filled with men and women electioneering through loud speakers and with noise-makers.

Party circulars were hurled out. "Cast your ballots. Vote for Herut and fight for Israel on both sides of the Jordan."

"Vote for the United Religious Bloc and make religion and tradition the basis of government and law!"

"Vote for the Mapam, the United Labor Party."

"Vote for Mapai and bring social welfare, health and security to all workers."

Last minute identity cards were being distributed to people who had neglected to get theirs before.

"I wish I could vote!" said Daniel.

"If I were eighteen and old enough to vote, I wouldn't wait until the last minute to get my card. I'd get ready the first thing. Abba did. He carries it in his bill-fold and guards it as a precious possession."

But that was yesterday. Today was Election Day, a national holiday. It was so quiet. No more electioneering, no more motor caravans, sound trucks, shouting men and women touring the city! The government had forbidden all rallies and campaigning beginning at midnight. A calm descended over the country. It really was a holiday. No one went to work. The factories and stores were closed. In each city and village, polling places were set up. The sun was shining brightly as long queues of voters lined up and waited to cast their ballots.

All inhabitants of voting age were out. Arab and Jewish citizens voted together. For the first time the people of Israel was expressing itself democratically.

David Ben Gurion and his wife rose early, and voted at a polling station in northern Tel Aviv. The night before, he had delivered his final talk over the radio, "Kol Israel," and had stressed Israel's policy of peace with her neighbors.

A group of orthodox Jews near one polling station began to chatter. Israel was really free, and they were free to vote! It was hard to believe!

Just as they were about to enter the station, they began

to recite the "Shehecheyanu," thanking God for permitting them to live to see this day.

A woman of seventy-two held up her identity card. She had come on an immigrant ship. "I must vote," she said, "it's the first time in my life, and perhaps the last."

The Arab men were excited. This was their very first election too. In Nazareth, during Harem hours, heavily-veiled Arab women, otherwise not permitted to appear in public, emerged from their homes to vote. Each voter presented his card to the election committee, received an envelope and entered a booth to cast his vote.

The new government of Israel gradually moved out of its provisional status to full-fledged nationhood—young—strong—determined.

"I wonder who's going to win," said Naomi. "The Labor Party under David Ben Gurion? Or Mapam under Yitshak Tabenkin?"

"Do you think that Menachim Begin, leader of Irgun Tzvai Leumi has a large following?" asked Daniel. "You know, they now call themselves the Freedom Party and insist that Israel reach over both sides of the Jordan."

"It was smart of the religious groups to unite. That way they have a better chance of getting representation."

"Let's go up to City Hall and look at the election returns. Some of them must be in. They must be posted outside the building," said Daniel.

It didn't take much urging to get Avram and Naomi to join Daniel. They were very anxious to know. But they weren't the only ones that had that bright idea. A crowd had already gathered to watch the City Clerk post the latest returns.

"Only Tel Aviv and Jaffa reports are listed on this side. Here Mapai has 34%; Herut 16.3%; Religious Bloc 13.4%; Mapam 9.4%; General Zionists 7%; Progressives 4.6%; Sephardi 2.5%; Communists 2.6%."

"The Jerusalem results are still incomplete," Daniel noted.

"The totals are over here on this side," Avram called. "Mapai is leading with 34.4%, and look the Religious Bloc has 13.6%."

"But all the votes aren't in yet," said Naomi.

"Of course not," answered Daniel. "The troops haven't been heard from. It'll take some time before their votes are counted."

"They should arrive in a day or two, but do you think they will affect the final results very much? I wonder whether there are more Herut and Mapam voters in the army than among the civilians."

"We'll find out soon enough. David Ben Gurion's party is so far ahead that I'm sure he's in. Looks like we'll have another ruler named David."

"Well," said Daniel, "King David widened Israel's borders in the days of the Bible. David will strengthen the borders of Israel in our day."

"Let me tell you something about this founding father of Israel who will probably be its first Premier. He may not be very tall, but he is truly great. His life story is written in this pamphlet that was issued by Mapai before the elections."

They had reached the Bialik Museum, across the square from the City Hall. They sat on the stone ledge in front of the building. Naomi opened the pamphlet.

"David Ben Gurion was born in Poland in 1886, in the days when the name of Theodore Herzl was already well known. He learned about Zionism in the home of his father, and as a youngster began to dream about Erets Yis-rael. Early in the 20th century, when Palestine was still under Turkish rule, Ben Gurion came to Israel in the second Aliyah.

"As a Chaluts, he labored in the orchards of Petakh Tikvah, in the wine cellars of Rishon L'Zion, and in the fields of Galilee. Often he was hungry and lonesome. He contracted malaria from which so many of the early settlers died. He was one of the early Shomrim who guarded the frontiers day and night.

"In 1912 he went to Constantinople to study law, because he thought he would be more useful to his people if he knew law. Little did he realize to what extent this training would prepare him for his great political future.

"Ben Gurion visited the United States in 1914, just as the first World War began. He was an idealist, who dreamed about a Palestine once again belonging to the Jewish people. He was a man of peace. He didn't like war. But when they were recruiting soldiers for the Jewish Legion, he joined, and even recruited others, because the United States prom-ised to free Palestine from the Turks."

"We all know what happened after that," Avram added. "The British received the Mandate over Palestine."

But Naomi continued. "As a youth, Ben Gurion was

active in the organization of the Histadrut, serving as its
general secretary for a number of years. At the eighteenth
World Zionist Congress, he was elected a member of the
World Zionist Executive. His magnetic personality at-
tracted many followers. He formed the heHaluts movement
in America. Ben Gurion was one of the founders of Kupat
Kholim, a health organization. A great lover of books, he
helped foster the cultural life of Israel and stimulated Histadrut to organize a network of libraries to bring books and
reading material to the people. He was himself the author
of a number of books. When he isn't working he is studying.
His hobby is Greek history."

"I remember reading an essay of Ben Gurion's in school,"
said Daniel slowly, wrinkling his brow as he spoke. "I recall
our teacher telling us that he sounded like a prophet. He
reminded us that Jews in the days of the Phoenicians were
sailors and fishermen. He also reminded us of Zevulun, the
sailor tribe, that settled on the shores of the Mediterranean.
He said that some day the Jews would again be sailors and
that boats manned by Jews would once more plow the
seven seas."

"Yes," continued Avram, "I also remember reading a
book he wrote called *Our Neighbors and We*. It was about
better understanding between Arabs and Jews. Yes, David
Ben Gurion always has been a great leader."

"He certainly has," Naomi added. "It was really his vision
and his courage that spurred our people."

"The story of his life and his deeds is really the story of
the Jewish State," Daniel concluded.

The people of Israel looked upon Ben Gurion as the symbol of living Israel,

14. Tu B'Shvat—
A Double Holiday Now

FEBRUARY 14, 1949 was a double holiday in new
Israel. Not only was it Tu B'Shvat, the Jewish
Arbor Day, when everyone planted a tree, but it
was also Knesset Day when the Israel Parliament was meeting for the first time in two thousand years.

The new, democratically-elected Knesset consisted of 120
members like its predecessor the Knesset haG'dolah of olden
times. Nineteen trade union officials, eighteen writers
(newspapermen, novelists, poets, etc.), twelve lawyers, ten
business men, eight politicians, five rabbis, five manual

laborers, and about thirty-five farmers, three bank directors, two mayors, two teachers and one university professor comprised it. Eleven members were women. Three were Arabs.

On that memorable day Jerusalem was, of course, in a festive mood. Everywhere blue-white flags were proudly fluttering in the wind.

Jerusalem itself had not been assigned to the Jews in the original U.N. Resolution of November 29th. It was still the subject of international controversy. But when the Arabs laid siege to Jerusalem and tried to starve it out, who defended the city? When the Arabs bombed the sacred shrines, who protected them? Not the Moslems and not the Christians, and not the United Nations! The Jews were the sole defenders of the Eternal City and its hallowed places.

By choosing Jerusalem as the Knesset site, the Israeli were telling the world that they would not forsake their capital. There was no doubt about the real meaning of their choice. But because the Knesset convened there, a number of diplomatic representatives were absent. Forty-two nations had recognized Israel and most of them sent envoys to Jerusalem. But the American, British and French officials stayed away because their governments could not yet accept this decision.

Not only Jerusalem, but the whole country assumed a festive atmosphere. It seemed as though every rock and stone, every hill and valley, every tree and every flower seemed aware of the glory this Tu B'Shvat brought.

Daniel and his brothers were on their way to Jerusalem. They knew they couldn't get into the Agency Building for the opening of the Knesset. Visitors were admitted by invitation only.

Everyone who could possibly do so made the pilgrimage to Jerusalem that day. They travelled by bus, and everyone was gay. Everywhere there were posters bearing quotations from the Bible, and slogans of celebration.

Daniel stood up to let an old man with a long white beard sit near the window. "Do you know why I am going to Jerusalem?" the old man asked. "I suffered for many years in Poland. I was lucky to be rescued by Israel. I had to come to Jerusalem to see with my own eyes the leaders of the nation gather for haKnesset haG'dolah."

A young soldier sitting across from them answered, "I feel privileged too. I am the son of an old settler in Galil. I have a two-day furlough. Instead of going home I'm going to Jerusalem. Only once in a lifetime . . . no, once in two thousand years, does one have such an opportunity. I just couldn't miss it."

The bus rolled along at a rapid pace. Jeep after jeep filled with singing soldiers passed on the road.

Cars filled with children were on their way to Jerusalem for the great event. They were going up also for the tree planting ceremonies.

Not so long ago, on these very roads, Arab bullets had shot at every Jew who came that way. But now it was different. The road had been cleared of the marauders! The road to Jerusalem was free!

"Think back to what was happening only a year ago," reminisced the soldier. "Israel was a battlefield. Seven Arab states were going to pounce upon us. The Syrians were about

to enter Mishmar haYarden. The Lebanese planned to
swoop down on Haifa. The forces of Transjordan stood
ready to attack the settlements in the Valley of Yizrael. The
Iraqi troops stood ready to cut through from Tulkarem
to Natanya and the sea. The Egyptians and the Yemenites
were ready to advance from Rafa to Tel Aviv, and through
Beersheba and Hebron to Jerusalem. The Arab Legion was
also threatening Jerusalem on the Jericho side, hoping to
make its way down the Jaffa Road to Tel Aviv. All we had
were light arms and an underground army, with nothing at
our backs but the sea.

"Armed guerilla bands swooped down on the convoys.
Snipers lay in ambush to murder innocent civilians. 'Hired'
Arab soldiers streamed across the borders and besieged
poorly-defended settlements. And this very Jerusalem was
cut off from food and water and surrounded by the enemy."

"Just a year ago it looked as though the world had
abandoned us," said Daniel. "England was putting all kinds
of political road blocks in our path."

"But Israel acted bravely," continued the soldier. "Our
leaders were determined to fight back. Besides we had no
other choice. So we fought stubbornly, and didn't yield an
inch of ground. Remember that 'Burma Road' we built to
bring food and water to the trapped Jerusalemites? We
drove the enemy out of our country, all right. The Arab
armies were routed, and our tiny army was victorious."

"You sound like a history book," said Daniel.

"We're approaching the city," said the soldier pointing.
"See those small houses over the mountain? That means
we're on the outskirts of Jerusalem."

"Yes, we're almost there," breathed the old man.

"What's that big sign over the gate? What does it say?" asked Daniel.

"Oh, I can read it JE-RU-SA-LEM!—Yes, Jerusalem—is—our—Stronghold!"

Jerusalem was suitably dressed for the holiday. Even the houses looked different. Their pink stone fronts still retained evidences of bombing. Flags fluttered from every roof-top and from every window. People gathered in the streets, waiting for the big parade.

Children were marching in a parade of their own. Leading them was a band with drums beating and bugles blaring. Where could they be going? It was too early to go to the Knesset opening.

"Don't you know?" asked Daniel a little impatiently. "Can't you see what they are carrying?"

"Oh yes," Avram replied, "saplings, baby trees to plant."

"Of course, it's Tu B'Shvat. I wonder where they are going?

"To Mount Herzl. Don't you see what it says on the banners!"

And the banners proudly proclaimed: "We honor the heroes who fell in battle." "We commemorate the defenders of the Holy City."

All along the highway between Tel Aviv and Jerusalem, these tree-planting ceremonies were conducted. Many of the trees would serve to commemorate fallen heroes, for even in the midst of their jubilation, the people grieved over their losses.

"Our trees will honor our heroes."

David Ben Gurion was there to console the mourners. Even he, the fighter, could not finish his speech of dedication. His voice faltered as he choked back the tears.

The Kaddish was recited. The planters raised their spades to plant their saplings. And when the Kaddish was completed, a low wail broke out as one of the mothers bent down to plant her tree.

All over the country similar scenes were taking place. Millions of trees were planted to commemorate the defenders who fell in the War of Independence.

Now the parade passed the stately Yeshurun Synagogue. And then they passed the police stations! Only nine months ago they had been covered by barbed wire fences.

But the barbed wire was gone, and now blue-white flags were seen instead.

The bus stopped near the Yeshurun Synagogue, a circular structure built of Jerusalem stone.

And who was that coming?

"Look," called Daniel, "it's Rabbi Isaac haLevi Herzog, Rabbi Uzziel, the Chief Rabbis." And most of the rabbinate of Jerusalem were following them.

"And who's that in the silk hat?"

"Why that's Moshe Sharett; how odd he looks in such a hat!'

The great dignitaries of the Jewish State were stopping for worship.

Time passed quickly. It was nearly four o'clock, the hour set for the opening of Knesset. The meeting was to take place in the Jewish Agency Building almost across the way. The wide entrance had been roped off, and only officials and a selected number of guests were admitted. Some came by foot from the Yeshurun Synagogue, and others by motor car. Military police stood at attention, and the combined Police-Army Band played.

Suddenly the crowd surged forward. The head of the government was approaching! The crowd began to applaud and to shout. "Long live Ben Gurion!" "Long live Ben Gurion." And then: Dah-gale Shek! Present Arms!

The soldiers lifted their rifles and fired. One of the officers raised his sword, the signal for the band to play. Hearts were throbbing with joy and sorrow. They were happy to have lived to see this day.

Dr. Chaim Weizmann, head of the provisional government arrived. He was met at the city entrance by a guard of honor.

"This is the man whom the Jews delight to honor," said Daniel, as the fleet of cars went by. Thousands of people cheered wildly as his entourage passed.

"Chaim Weizmann lifted his hat to us," said the soldier. "Doesn't Mrs. Weizmann look like a queen? So regal! So stately!"

Chaim Weizmann arrived at the Agency Building, followed by others, members of the government. They were greeted by a round of applause. All rose to their feet. The band began to play as they sang the song of eternal hope.

From the ceiling were suspended two large Eternal Lights, one Ner Tamid to remember the Jews who perished at the hands of the Nazis, the other to remember the soldiers who gave their lives so that Israel might live.

Everyone was stirred. Even Chaim Weizmann brushed

away a tear. Loud speakers carried the strains of the Hatikva to the waiting throng, who spontaneously joined in the singing. The Shofar proclaimed the day of freedom. The prayers of generations were fulfilled!

Yes, for generations Jews had prayed, "Sound a loud blast on the Shofar to announce our freedom." Today the Shofar was sounded, and the prayer recited. "Sound the great Trumpet for our freedom, lift the ensign to gather the exiles, and gather us from the four corners of the earth. Blessed art Thou O Lord, Who gatherest the banished ones of Thy people Israel."

Chaim Weizmann opened the Knesset, the first Jewish Parliament. It was a momentous speech. He reminded his people of the great prophecy. "Remnants return," he said. "And since we are but the fraction of a remnant, double responsibility is placed upon us to fill the terrible void in our national life created by the slaughter of the best sons of our people."

Weizmann recalled the great leaders who had blazed the trail: Theodore Herzl, the father of political Zionism, Henrietta Szold, the mother of Youth Aliyah, Menahem Ussishkin, the redeemer of the land . . . and the others who had envisioned the Jewish State.

15. A Long and Difficult Road

IT was after midnight. The telephone rang in the home of Dr. Weizmann in Rehovot. A sleepy voice answered. It was the voice of Chaim Weizmann.

"Shalom, this is Yigal Kimkhi, your secretary, speaking. I'm sorry to disturb you at this late hour."

"What's wrong? Did something happen?"

"Something wonderful has happened," Kimkhi responded. "May I extend to you a Mazal Tov." I have the honor to inform you that the Knesset has just elected you President of the State of Israel."

There was silence at the other end of the wire for a moment. Then Chaim Weizmann, in a somewhat unsteady voice, answered, "Thank you. Thank you very much." And that was all.

Early the next morning, a caravan of motor cars was seen coming down the south Jerusalem road. A committee of twelve, symbolizing the twelve tribes of Biblical Israel, and Speaker Yoseph Sprinzak and two aides, were on their way to Rehovot. They had been delegated officially to inform Chaim Weizmann of his election, and to personally escort him back to Jerusalem for the inauguration.

The entourage finally pulled up in front of Dr. Weizmann's home, on a high hill, overlooking the countryside. The delegation entered the house and was ushered into the spacious library. It was a cold morning. They grouped themselves around the fireplace and waited.

In a few moments, the door opened and Dr. Weizmann entered, dressed simply in a dark suit. He seated himself in the armchair near the fireplace.

The delegation formed a semi-circle around him. Yoseph Sprinzak, head of the delegation, spoke:

"Chaim ben Ozer and Rachel Weizmann, we represent the different groups of the nation. We have been instructed by Knesset Israel to inform you that last night, at midnight, you were elected the first President of Israel. We have orders to escort you to the Holy City. You will take your oath of office in the presence of Knesset."

Chaim Weizmann, pale, deeply stirred, rose:

"Words fail me, my dear Yoseph, at this historic moment. A great responsibility has been placed upon my shoulders.

I will try, with all of my strength, to fulfill the great obligation that comes at the twilight of my life. Accept my sincere thanks. God bless you all."

The President shook hands with each member of the delegation. When he approached the Arab delegate, the Arab bent over and kissed the hand of the President, as is the custom among his people.

Soon they were ready to leave. The President was accompanied by his wife. The delegation left for Jerusalem.

The news spread that the President was coming to be inaugurated. The city buzzed with excitement. There hadn't been a real Jewish ruler in Jerusalem since the days of the Maccabees. "Did you hear?" whispered a little girl. "Do you know?" said one little Hassid to his friend.

The word got around that the President was on his way.

No one attended school. No one reported for work. This was the day of days—the first inauguration in Israel.

One little yeshiva bachur, with curly "paot," was so excited he jumped up and down for joy. Suddenly he stood still. "Today is a day to praise God. We should recite Psalms." And in the open street of the Holy City, he began to chant the Shir haMaalot. An old man nearby joined him. Others did too. Soon all the people around him were fervently chanting Psalms.

The procession approached the gates of the city.

The entire entourage walked to the gate, where a ribbon was stretched across the road. Here the mayor of Jerusalem and his council greeted the President. The President cut the ribbon as a symbol that Jerusalem could not be severed from Israel.

The mayor handed the President the keys to the city. "Right here," the mayor said, "right at this very spot, in 1917, the Turks surrendered to the British conqueror, General Allenby. Today we have the honor, Mr. President, to give the keys of the city to you."

The procession continued along the flag-draped streets of Jerusalem through the Gates of Triumph.

The streets were already lined with people. In the procession were military police on motorcycles, and jeeps packed with steel-helmeted soldiers who had fought the war for liberation.

Rows and rows of happy soldiers, from every branch of service, stood rigidly at attention. Boy scouts were marching.

A boy and a girl approached the President's car. They had flowers for the First Lady. The procession stopped. The children made their presentation, and the parade continued. Flowers and garlands were tossed to the Presidential car all along the way. People shouted: "Long live the President!"

"The President is coming! The President is coming!"

The procession halted before the Jewish Agency Building. At its entrance stood a police unit carrying flag-topped spears. The lines broke, but order was immediately restored. The President of Israel emerged. "Dah-gal Shek!" The rifle shots rang clear and loud. Heavy silence filled the atmospere. The band played the strains of Hatikva. The President leaned heavily on the arm of his wife. He was deeply stirred by this reception. Then the cheers: "Long live the President! Long life to the President of Israel!"

He seemed rooted to the ground. Here stood Chaim Weizmann . . . proud yet humble in this day of fulfillment.

And what happened inside the Jewish Agency Building? All we know is what we heard over the loud speaker.

The President of Israel entered the Assembly Room of the Jewish Agency Building. The entire Knesset rose.

The Shofar calls T'ki-ah! Sh'varim! T'ruah! T'ki-ah G'dolah! reverberated. Everyone was so excited.

A rabbi recited the Shehecheyanu, thanking God for permitting them to live to reach this day.

Yoseph Sprinzak, Speaker of the Knesset, declared "Mr. President, we now proceed to swear you into office. I will now read you the text of the oath."

Weizmann rose. He lifted a trembling hand and repeated, "I, Chaim ben Ozer Weizmann as president of the State, do swear allegiance to the State of Israel, and to its law."

During this ceremony, a twenty-one gun salute was fired throughout Israel. "Long live the President! Long live the President!" The crowd went wild amid cheering, kissing, laughing . . . and crying.

The excitement subsided. The members of the Knesset returned to their seats. Weizmann continued, "Greetings to the Jewish people throughout the world. I am fully aware of the responsibility I now assume. The task that has been entrusted to me is grave indeed. What we do here, or what we do not do here, will bring light or shadow to our entire nation. This is a great hour in my life."

He recalled the names of those who had died so that Israel might live. Many sobbed. The President paused. Once it seemed as though he could not continue. Scarcely a person had not lost someone dear to him in the war.

Such a variety of people attended this historic meeting. Rabbinical dignitaries, Arabs in tarbush and kafiyah, smartly-dressed women, diplomats wearing striped trousers next to deputies in open shirts. Then Chaim Weizmann called on each deputy to take the oath. Each in turn responded when his name was called.

After his address, Dr. Weizmann shook hands with most of the members of the Knesset. Among the first was Muhammed Edin Seif, an Arab.

Chaim Weizmann moved toward the exit, his head lowered. "It has been a long and difficult road."

The crowd continued shouting, "Long life to the President of Israel!"

It had indeed been a long and difficult road for Chaim Weizmann. Born in Russia in the village of Motele, near the town of Pinsk, he was the third of a family of fifteen children. Even as a child, he was affected by the persecution of Russian Jews. Jews were not allowed to go to public school in Russia. He had to go to another country to study chemistry. He graduated from the University of Berlin. Even then he distinguished himself as a skillful debater.

Weizmann's first position was that of a lecturer in Geneva, Switzerland. Here he met Vera, a medical student, who later became his wife. By this time he could speak not only Russian, German, Hebrew, Yiddish and French, but also English. It was not long before he accepted a lectureship at Manchester, England, where he met Lord Balfour, a member of the British Parliament.

At one time, during a conversation, Balfour suggested that the Jews accept Britain's offer to settle in an African colony. And Weizmann asked, "Suppose England were offered Paris for London. Would you accept?" "But we already have London," Balfour answered. "But," replied Weizmann, "the Jews had Jerusalem when London was but a marsh."

In the course of the next ten years, Weizmann not only worked hard in his laboratory. He continued to devote himself to the cause of Zionism.

Then came the first World War. The shortage of acetone in England was alarming. Munitions could not be manufactured. Chaim Weizmann worked day and night. The need was very urgent. Finally, Weizmann developed a method to make acetone.

Lloyd George, then Prime Minister, offered him personal recognition and honors. Weizmann would accept no personal honors.

"There is nothing I want for myself, but there is something I would like you to do for my people."

Shortly thereafter the Balfour Declaration (1917) was issued.

Thus Weizmann helped make possible the first step in the realization of the hope and dream for a Jewish homeland. After World War I, the League of Nations decreed that Palestine was to become the homeland of the Jewish people. Britain became the Mandatory Power to help establish that homeland.

Weizmann attended every Zionist Congress except the first one in 1897. In those days he was too poor to pay for the trip. He worked his way across Europe to Basle, Switzerland, where Theodore Herzl and his followers were meeting for the first time. But he arrived two days too late. It was at the Sixth Congress in 1903, that he stood up to oppose Herzl on the same issue he had argued with Lord Balfour. Herzl was almost persuaded to accept Uganda in Africa. Weizmann led the opposition. He declared that the Jewish people would accept no place other than Erets Yisrael even as a temporary refuge.

In 1920, after many years of devoted service, Chaim Weizmann was elected President of the World Zionist Organization. This was a great honor. He was frequently criticized, but he continued to work for the cause.

In 1925, another Weizmann dream became real. He saw Hebrew University on Mt. Scopus dedicated. Lord Balfour and hundreds of other dignitaries came to take part in the festivities marking the dedication.

Dr. Weizmann established a home and a laboratory in Rehovot, a colony near Tel Aviv. There the Zieff Institute and later also the Weizmann Institute became centers for research and scientific experiment. He lived to see the day when the Hebrew University, the Zieff and the Weizmann Institutes were united with a common Board of Directors, headed by the world renowned scientist, Albert Einstein.

Weizmann created the Jewish Agency. He wanted all the Jewish people to be represented. Therefore, the membership from all over the world contained non-Zionists as well as Zionists.

In 1931 he was forced to retire from the presidency of the World Zionist Congress because its members were impatient for immediate results. But Chaim Weizmann continued to work in the ranks for his people.

He served a second term as President of the Jewish Agency in 1935. The outbreak of Arab disturbances in 1936 made his burden heavier. And on the political front, he had to contend with British policies. The Peel Royal Commission recommended partition of Palestine, which Weizmann was ready to accept. But this position was violently challenged on the floor of the Congress. During his administration, the White Paper of 1939 restricting immigration and the purchase of land was issued. He suffered deeply when English officials turned refugees from the shores of the Promised Land to perish in the sea. Despite the White Paper, Weizmann continued to support large-scale settlement in the Holy Land.

It was a long and difficult road to travel, but at long last the goal was attained. Israel had emerged victorious in battle. The era of British rule ended. Israel had come into being and had written a fitting postscript to the saga of the struggle for national existence by making Chaim Weizmann its first President.

The day after his inauguration, Chaim Weizmann returned to Rehovot, to his first love—science. Relaxed, surrounded by friends, and in the tranquility of the Institute, he met with his staff of co-workers.

"Just as the law came forth from Zion, so will science," he declared. "The Weizmann Institute is not only a center of science, but a bulwark of the State. Science has played a great part in the redemption of the country's wilderness, and especially the Negev. It is our task to make the Negev as well as the rest of our nation fruitful again."

Dr. Weizmann always looked ahead.

And it was morning, and it was evening, the fourth day after the creation of the Jewish State. Chaim Weizmann, seventy-four-year-old statesman, had become the President of the State of Israel. And the people of Israel saw that it was good, and they were glad.

16. The Paths
Our Fathers Trod

IT was on October 15, 1948 that the Egyptians invaded the Negev. They used the very roads that their ancestors had used thousands of years ago, when at the famous battle of Megiddo, in 609 B.C.E., one of the Pharaohs badly defeated the army of Judea under King Josiah.

It was in the fifth year of King Rehoboam that Shayshik, King of Egypt, attacked Jerusalem. Twelve hundred chariots, and sixty thousand horsemen, and countless other troops thundered up to Jerusalem with him.

Two thousand years later, through the same ancient cities, the Egyptians again came up, this time to fight the new Israel. When the Israel soldiers returned to Ayalon (Latrun), they fought in the same places that their ancestors had fought in the days of Joshua ben Nun to the days of the Maccabees.

In ancient days the Egyptians came by chariot; today the vehicles were modern ones. In those days they set out to build forts; now they tried to establish defenses. But the problem of keeping supply lines open was still the same.

Anyone with a knowledge of military science knows that similar situations create similar results. The Egyptians used the same approaches for their military invasion that their ancestors had used thousands of years ago. But the Israel soldiers knew their Bible well. No wonder they stopped the invader so quickly. They had only to follow the action set down in the Bible. The Israelis surrounded and trapped the Egyptians in Al Faluja, just at the Egyptian-Israel frontier, cutting off the Egyptian columns and clinching the Negev campaign.

To control the road from Jerusalem to Elat, the army had to capture the pivotal point of Beersheba, which for centuries had been the meeting place of camel caravans as they passed from Syria to Egypt, from Egypt to Canaan, from Geza to Arabia. Beersheba means "the well of the Seven" since Abraham had dug a well here and had given Abimelech, the Philistine, seven ewe lambs to seal his right to the place. Beersheba played an important part in ancient days . . . and it again was destined to play a his-

toric role in the new Israel. Beersheba must be taken . . .
and held!

Yigal Yadin, the Chief of Operations, who later became
Rav Aloof (Commander in Chief) of the Israel Army, had
mapped the campaign which halted the Egyptians and
brought the Arabs to terms.

Only thirty-three years of age, Yadin was a great soldier
and an important military man.

Yigal had studied archeology when he was a little boy,
and not just because his father was a teacher of that subject
at the Hebrew University. He had two brothers, one an
actor, the other a flyer. Mati, the aviator, flew out of Tel
Aviv in pursuit of Egyptian planes, never to return. When
the boys were small, their father would take them on
tiyulim through the ancient city of Jerusalem. Little did
Yadin dream that the knowledge he acquired in traveling
to the Dead Sea, through the Judean Desert, would stand
him in good stead when he became a defender in Haganah
and a soldier in the Israel Army.

Yigal graduated from the Hebrew University. He became an authority on archeology. He delivered lectures and
wrote articles. His most notable book is called *The Army of
Israel in the Biblical Period*.

Later he realized that his study of archeology had prepared him to be a better soldier. He often said that there
was but one difference between the two careers—in archeology, you look to the past; in war, you look to the future.

He started his military career as a member of Haganah.
He became Commander of Kiryat Anavim, and later of the
isolated and dangerous K'far Etzion. He was trained by

the British Colonel Orde Wingate, a good friend of the Jews, who taught many of our boys to fight.

Orde Wingate was an Englishman, an Englishman who knew his Bible. He loved the Bible and the land where the people of the Bible lived. Although it was very difficult for him, he learned to speak Hebrew and was amazed to find that there were Jews in Palestine who didn't know the language. As an officer in the British Army, he would frequently travel through the country. Yadin loved to travel with him, for Wingate would always make the Bible come to life. He would quote passage after passage from it. "Here is the plough of the Goyim." "Here Deborah and Barak met." "On these Gilboa Mountains, Saul encamped." All were an open book to him. He would point to the rocks where the army hid and where they escaped to the valley. He would talk about the wars, and fight the battles as if they had been fought but yesterday.

When Yigal joined the British Army during World War II, he fought as Colonel Wingate had taught him. It didn't take long for him to become a staff commander at the planning office of the British Army Anthers Division.

No wonder, then, that Rav Aloof Yadin was Chief of Operations of the Israel Army. No wonder, then, that he understood, too, from his studies, the ways of the invading Egyptian Army and knew how to head them off.

The Israelis received training from an American army officer too. He was David (Mickey) Marcus, a West Point graduate. He was one of America's most brilliant strategists. Having fought in every theater of Europe, he was asked to come to Israel to help.

Marcus came to Israel and taught the eager Jewish lads what he had learned at West Point. He taught them how to use guns and bullets. He helped them organize the army and taught them to defend the land. The Israel boys learned to love and revere him. When the Arabs stood at the borders of Israel, it was Colonel Marcus who led them to victory.

One day, while Colonel Marcus was checking the lookout posts, he was killed. The entire Israel Army mourned him, for they had lost a true friend. The body of Colonel David Marcus was escorted to the United States by an Israel Guard of Honor. He was buried with all honors at West Point.

The war was over. The Arabs had been brought to terms, and both sides were negotiating an armistice. Yigal Yadin had worked hard.

Yadin stood pat on the terms. He demanded a strong military position in the eastern Negev on the ground that Jordan or Britain might attack from that side. He must have Beersheba! Beersheba must again be the crossroads, the strategic meeting place for modern commerce.

And so, skillful diplomacy, coupled with stubborn resistance, won the Negev. And Rav Aloof Yigal Yadin was one of the signers of this historic Israel-Egyptian armistice!

In the Bible we read the story of how little David won a battle against a towering giant using only a sling shot. Today we read the story of how little Israel won a battle against the Egyptian Army with strong heart and clever action. The British "Goliath" gave the Arabs arms and money. "David's" weapon was love of country. The tiny state had vanquished the enemy and pursued the retreating invaders. No wonder people were saying, "Never has so much been accomplished with so little, by so few."

But there were other borders to be settled. Other armistices had to be signed with Lebanon, Jordan and Syria. This would require a long time and much negotiation. The Israelis were willing to discuss these matters, but the Arabs were stubborn.

And so two ancient peoples, the descendants of Isaac and the descendants of Isaac's brother Ishmael were brought together in peace by an American Negro, Dr. Ralph Bunche of the United Nations. Thus came true the words of the prophet Malachi: "One God created us, One Father over all."

17. Open for Business

THE moment the Declaration of Independence was signed, the Israel government set itself up for business.

Postage stamps were immediately printed bearing the word "Israel." Daniel bought these stamps with the Hebrew letters on them, pasted them on envelopes and mailed them to himself. He wanted to keep the postmarked stamps as souvenirs forever.

"How lucky we are to see the new state being created," said Daniel to his brothers. "But we're not starting like the pioneers of America, with huge territories to be cultivated and just a few people to do the work."

"No," answered Shimshon, "ours is a small country, stony, swampy and desert. We have so many, many people to take care of. We have thousands of people to bring home, to help settle. So our beginning is quite different from America's."

First the government had to establish itself.

The first official act of the Premier was to revoke the White Paper. Thus he opened the gates of the new Israel to all who wanted to come to their old-new Homeland. By thousands and tens of thousands they came. They had to be absorbed. Housing had to be provided, work projects had to be planned.

Engineers, architects, construction experts began large-scale housing units. Town-planners tried to keep the new plans within the bounds of beauty and community well-being.

The infant state also had to get on its feet financially. It turned to America for international loans. They launched bond issues so that the Jews of the world could invest in Israel's economy. These were bought by Jews and non-Jews throughout the world as evidence of their faith in the future of Israel.

As the wheels of the government began to turn, the Israel Department of Education opened new schools. Many of them were schools in Arab villages. Then began the process of orientation of the newcomers. Courses in Hebrew were established for those who required basic education to make up for the many skipped years. Ulpan classes were organized for lawyers, doctors, teachers, dentists, engineers, so that the language would not be an obstacle to them in the new land.

Transportation was one of the difficult problems the new state had to tackle.

In olden times caravan routes formed the network of travel throughout the land. The new department of transportation gradually handled an increasing volume of passenger and commercial traffic.

The Yishuv uses buses and taxis to get about on tree-lined highways. For longer trips, travelers reserve "a seat" in a taxi which takes them from place to place.

One of the government's proudest acquisitions is an air line of its own, called El Al. El Al's planes are distinguished by the Hebrew lettering and the large Magen David emblazoned on them. The pilot, stewardess and the personnel also sport the Magen David on their natty blue uniforms.

The wheels of industry too were oiled for action.

Industrial ventures were launched. Manufacture increased. Kaiser Frazer automobies began to stream out of a large factory. American tire companies and shoe companies established plants. Investors from the world over have created a new thriving commerce in Israel.

Agricultural areas were made more productive by the establishment of a system of water-lines from Dan to Elat.

Factories for mass production of steel projects, for sugar (using sugar beets grown in the Emek), for furniture, for plastics and for fertilizer sprung up throughout the country. While all these new projects were getting under way,

Israel's citrus industry continued to export millions of cases of fruit.

The wheels of progress didn't decrease their speed as the repatriation and the redemption of the Jewish communities of the world continued. More work for more people— speeding up construction of houses, widening roads, laying new ones, planting saplings, setting up a network of pipelines and canals. Digging for copper and oil and manganese absorbed hundreds of workers especially in the Negev, dreariest spot in Israel, destined to become its brightest sector.

Towns and cities, sabras and new olim, capital and labor all working together to advance the ideals established by the Histadrut.

Meanwhile the new government exchanged envoys with the nations of the world. Even England, the recent foe, extended recognition quickly, and soon an Israeli representative was functioning in London.

Mordecai Eliash was the first Israeli Ambassador to England. He must have felt very much as John Adams, the first United States Ambassador, felt when that American revolutionary presented his credentials to King George III. Thus history repeated itself. Mr. Adams was graciously received by King George III. Almost two hundred years later, Mr. Eliash was graciously received by King George VI.

Diplomatic recognitions were quickly followed by trade agreements between Israel and the various nations.

Independence meant a new chapter in the history of the celebrated Histadrut. What is Histadrut? Its full title is

Histadrut haOvdim, which means General Federation of Labor. There were labor unions in America, and in other parts of the world too, but this Union was different. This group believed that pioneers should be helped not only to be true workers of the soil, but to be independent. They believed that a worker's rights and welfare should always be protected. Histadrut was founded to make sure that the people would live by the principles of justice and righteousness proclaimed by the prophets of Israel.

Histadrut, with which most of the workers in Israel are affiliated, is the backbone of the nation. It established collective farms and cooperated in the buying and selling of foods and materials. Its cooperatives dealt in citrus marketing, home building and even in banking. Histadrut members fought in Haganah, the underground organization which defended and protected the people.

Histadrut also guarded the health of its members. Membership dues supported a Workers' Health Organization, the Kupat Kholim, which operated clinics, hospitals and sanatoria in every corner of Israel.

Thus Histadrut was largely responsible for the structure and organization of Israel's economy. It was important in building construction, in marketing of agricultural products, in industry, in transportation and even published a daily newspaper called "Davar." But always, in addition to its function as a labor union, it provided its membership with social welfare and cultural services.

Built on the principles of justice and righteousness proclaimed by the prophets, Histadrut daily brought into realization the prophecy of Amos:

"Behold, the days come," saith the Lord, "that the plowman shall overtake the reaper, and the treader of grapes, him that soweth the seed, and the mountains shall drop sweet wine and all the hills shall melt."

Before and after independence, Histadrut, through its far flung enterprises, sought to fulfill the words of Amos.

18. Am Yisrael Hay

THE 5th of Iyar came and went. A year passed since nations of the world had saluted the birth of Israel.

It had been a busy year. There was the Declaration of Independence, followed by diplomatic recognition from country after country.

There had been the war with the Arabs, there had been the elections, the sessions of the Knesset, the naming of a president. Then came the question of entering the United Nations.

Any people who sought peace, the U.N. Charter read,

could be admitted. Israel felt it was eligible. It had proved its ability to defend itself and to govern itself. Now it wanted to join the family of the nations. But each time Israel applied for membership, there was a delay. First it was Britain, who raised the question of the Arab refugees. Israel replied that the refugees had chosen to leave the country of their own free will. Then it was the Arab states which threw up obstacles. Bitterly did they oppose Israel's request, and some other countries accepted the Arab position charging that Israel was defying the Assembly plan for the internationalization of Jerusalem.

The year was running out. The hope that admission would come as a birthday present on the 5th of Iyar, was frustrated.

May 4th, the 5th of Iyar, came and went. Israel still waited on the doorstep of the United Nations.

Nonetheless, the anniversary was celebrated in Israel, and throughout the world too. People of all ages turned out for the festivities. Again the blue and white emblems were hoisted from the roof-tops and the balconies. On the buildings of almost every street hung huge portraits of Theodore Herzl.

There was a huge military parade in Jerusalem. Thousands of enthusiastic Jews watched it. In the reviewing stand stood Brigadier General Jacob Dori, the Israel Army's Chief of Staff, who took the salute. The parade included artillery units, mechanized companies, the home guard, and the Red Magen David units with their ambulances. Tank guns, sailors in white, paratroopers, and the fire brigade marched in colorful parade.

The people, in Shabbat clothes, were once more in a holiday mood. They jammed the streets. They filled the roof-tops and the balconies. They forgot, for the moment, the trials of the past. They even forgot, for the moment, the cares of the future. This was a glorious day.

From Dan to Elat, the flag of Israel fluttered a message of happiness on this day of commemoration. Everyone felt like a founding father.

A Thanksgiving service was conducted in the Yeshurun Synagogue.

The gaiety lasted into the night. At Zion Square, the police band provided the music. Spirits were high as everyone, young and old, joined in singing and dancing on this gala birthday party.

The school children of Tel Aviv demonstrated their joy in a picturesque parade to haKiryah, just outside the city. Here the Minister of Education greeted them. He told them that, in honor of Yom Atsmaut, Independence Day, a copy of the Israel Declaration of Independence would be presented to every schoolroom in the nation.

Then came May 11th. And in the United Nations the Arab nations made a last ditch effort against Israel. As the voting commenced the suspense mounted. Finally the count was tallied and lo!—it was thirty-seven to twelve in favor of Israel with nine countries abstaining. The pro-Israel vote was even higher than that for partition on November 29th. Thirty-seven nations had opened the door wide and extended a hearty welcome to the world's newest republic.

And so it came to pass, on May 11, 1949, the State of

Israel joined the family of nations and became the fifty-ninth country to add its flag to those of her sister lands.

Foreign Minister Moshe Sharett had flown to Lake Success from Tel Aviv. When the loud cheering over the result of the vote had subsided, Australia's Dr. Herbert V. Evatt, Assembly President, called the Israel Foreign Minister to the rostrum to be officially welcomed. The assembly had recognized that Israel was a "peace-loving state which accepts the obligation contained in the United Nations Charter and is able and willing to carry out those obligations."

"This is the day which the Lord hath made; let us rejoice and be glad in it!" This was the tenor of the joyous greeting between nation and nation . . . between friend and friend.

It was a day of triumph for the Jews of the world. After all the unhappy years, the Tabernacle of David that had fallen was lifted up, as Amos had prophesied. The exiles had returned. The people were planted in the land, no more to be plucked out therefrom.

But there remained the task of building on freedom's foundations. The responsibility of translating the great ideals into living reality was a continuing challenge. Israel had still to bring the wanderers home, "The tired, the poor, the hunted masses." Then work had to be found for them so that they might attain dignity and security. Then the newcomers could become an integral part in the drama of nation building. From every corner of the world they were coming home.

And Israel, which sought only peace, turned to its great task of settlement and peaceful living. For a long time, each colony would be a fortress with soldiers on duty, not for fighting, but for the maintenance of peace.

This is the story of the Third Jewish Commonwealth. The tyrants sought to destroy them, but failed.

Am Yisrael Hay
The Jewish People Lives On!

A Glossary of
Words-People-Places

ADLOYADA—(Refers to the state of giddiness a celebrant of Purim experiences so that he can't distinguish between the sound of Haman and Mordecai.) Name given to Carnival conducted at Purim time in Tel Aviv.

AHAD HA-AM (One of the people)—The pen name used by Asher Ginzburg, noted Zionist philosopher and author. He lived in Tel Aviv from 1921 until he died in 1927.

ALIYAH (Going up)—Immigration to Israel.

AM YISRAEL HAY—A song and a slogan, "The people of Israel yet lives!"

ASEFAT HA-NIVHARIM—Elected assembly.

ATLIT—A city in Israel.

AUSCHWITZ—Notorious Nazi extermination camp in Poland.

AYM HA-KVUTSOT—Mother colony.

BAB EL WAD—Arabic for "door to the valley."

BEN YEHUDAH, ELIEZER—Father of modern Hebrew, he was responsible for the adoption of Hebrew as the official language of Jewish Palestine.

BET YAAKOV L'HU V'NALHA (O house of Jacob, come, let us go)—A Biblical utterance used in the Torah service.

BIALIK, CHAIM NAHMAN—The most important Hebrew poet of modern times. He lived in Tel Aviv from 1922 until his death in 1934.

CHALUTS—Jewish pioneer.

DAVAR—The name of the official Histadrut newspaper.

EIN B'REIRAH—No choice, no alternative.

EL AL (To above, meaning "to the sky")—Name of Israel air line.

ELAT—City in the southernmost tip of the Negev.

EMEK—Refers to Emek Yizrael, the valley between Mount Carmel and Mount Tabor.

ERETS YISRAEL—Land of Israel.

GENIZAH (Hidden)—A place where long lost manuscripts have been discovered.

GEVERET—Miss.

HADAR HA-CARMEL (Majesty of the Carmel)—A suburb of Haifa.

HAHSHARA—Colony in which future settlers of Israel receive training and preparation.

HAIFA—Israel's chief port city.

HA-POEL (The worker)—The name of one of the Israeli sports organizations.

HASSID—A member of a Jewish sect called Hassidim, known for their religious fervor.

HATIKVA (The hope)—The national anthem of Israel.

HE-HALUTS MOVEMENT—The movement to bring halutsim (pioneers) to Israel.

HERMON—A high mountain in Syria that is snow-capped.

HERUT (Freedom)—The name of one of Israel's political parties.

HERZL, THEODORE—Known as the father of political Zionism.

HISTADRUT—Israel's principal labor organization.

HISTADRUT OVDIM—The General Federation of Labor in Israel. Usually known as Histadrut.

HOVEVEI TSIYON—Lovers of Zion, an early European Zionist movement.

HULEH—A marshy section in northern Israel being reclaimed.

IRGUN (ZVAI LEUMI)—The Jewish underground army who fought the British Mandatory Power in Palestine.

IYAR—The eighth month in the Jewish calendar. It was on the fifth of this month that Israel declared its independence.

JORDAN RIVER—This river rises in the hills of northern Israel and proceeds southward until it empties into the Dead Sea, the lowest spot in the world. The river is appropriately named Yarden, the descender.

JUDENSTAAT—German for Jewish State. The name of Herzl's book which launched political Zionism.

KADDISH—Prayer recited in memory of the dead; actually a prayer of praise to God.

KIBBUTS (Gathering)—A farm colony in which everything is equally shared.

KIBBUTS GALUYOT—Ingathering of the exiles.

KNESSET (Assembly)—The governing body of Israel.

KNESSET HA-G'DOLAH—A post-biblical council of Rabbis.

KNESSET YISRAEL—The Jewish community.

KOL YISRAEL (Voice of Israel)—The name of the Israeli Broadcasting System.

KUPAT KHOLIM—Sick benefit fund conducted by Histadrut.

KVUTSAH—A collective or communal settlement.

LIHYOT AM HOFSHEE B'ARTSENU—To be a free people in our own land.

MACCABEE—(The famous family which rescued Judea from the Syrian oppression in the second century.) Name of an Israeli sports organization.

MAPAI—Labor party of Israel. Word is formed from initials of full Hebrew name.

MAPAM—United Labor Party, left wing. Word is formed from initials of full Hebrew name.

MATTATAI (Broom)—Name of a theater in Israel.

M'DINAT YISRAEL—State of Israel.

MIR SEINEN DO ("We are here")—Name of a partisan song.

MIZRACH (East)—The direction where orthodox Jews turn for prayers.

MOSHAV OVDIM—A workers' settlement or colony.

MOSHAVAH—A village.

NATANYA—Name of a coastal city built by Germans.

NEGEV—The southern part of Israel, most of it desert which is being reclaimed.

NER TAMID—Everlasting light which is always left burning over the synagogue ark.

OHEL (Tent)—Name of a theatrical group in Israel.

OLIM—Those who go up, referring to immigrants.

PALMACH—Shock troops.

PAOT—Side-burns worn by pious Jews.

PIRKE OVOS—The Saying of the Fathers.

RATSINU, VERATSINU VE'EN ZOT AGGADAH—We willed it and we willed it and it is no fairy tale. Refers to words of Herzl, "If you will it, it is no legend."

SABRA—The fruit of the wild cactus that grows plentifully in Israel. Also a nickname for a native Israeli.

SHEHEHEYANU—A word in a prayer thanking God for permitting us to reach this day that is recited when something new is begun.

SHIMSHON—Samson, biblical judge and strong man.

SHIR HA-MAALOT—A song in praise of God. The phrase is from the Book of Psalms.

SHOMRIM—Watchmen.

SZOLD, HENRIETTA—The celebrated American woman who founded Hadassah.

TEL AVIV (Hill of spring)—Israel's largest city.

TIYUL—Hike, Outing. (Plural—Tiyulim).

T'KIAH, SH'VARIM—Two of the four calls of the Shofar sounds; a short blast, broken calls.

T'NUVAH—A cooperative distribution agency for dairy products.

TRUAH, T'KIAH G'DOLAH—The last two calls of the Shofar sounds; staccatto calls, a long blast.

TSORHANIA (Necessities)—A general store.

TU B'SHVAT—Abbreviation for Hamisha Asar B'shvat, the 15th of the month of Shvat, the Jewish Arbor Day. The letters "Tu" stand for 15.

ULPAN—A Hebrew school for adult immigrants.

VAAD HA-LEUMI—National Executive Council.

WADI—A dry valley that was formerly a river.

YARKON—A river in Israel.

YEHUDA HALEVI—A great Hebrew poet of the Golden Age.

YESHIVAH—A rabbinical school.

YESHIVAH BAHUR—A young man who attends a yeshivah.

YIZRAEL (God sows)—The name of a valley in Israel.

YOUTH ALIYAH—The youth immigration movement first sponsored by Hadassah.